GED
Skill Workbook Series

Mathematics 2

New Readers Press

C O N T E N T S

GED® Skill Workbook
Mathematics 2
ISBN 978-1-56420-512-4

Copyright © 2005 Trian Publishing Company
Distributed by New Readers Press
ProLiteracy's Publishing Division
1320 Jamesville Avenue, Syracuse, New York 13210
www.newreaderspress.com

Printed in the United States of America
9 8 7 6 5

Proceeds from the sale of New Readers Press materials support professional
development, training, and technical assistance programs of ProLiteracy
that benefit local literacy programs in the U.S. and around the globe.

Project Developer: Caren Van Slyke
Writer: Cathy Fillmore Hoyt
Editor: Kathy Osmus
Copy Editor: Jody Lynn Levine
Production: Jean Farley Brown
Art and Design: Karen Blanchard
Cover Design: Kimbrly Koennecke

Congratulations. You are studying to take the GED Tests in order to earn your high school equivalency certificate.

Since there is a lot of ground to cover in preparing for the test, we thought that we could help you by developing this *GED Skill* workbook series. The formula for GED success is as simple as *1–2–3*.

1. Evaluate, pages v–11

In school and in your GED class, you have studied much of what you need to know to pass the GED. You may be asking yourself, *What do I already know? What do I need to learn? What do the GED questions look like?*

In Part 1 of this book, you will take an inventory that will help you figure out where you are in your studies. After you check your answers, you will use the *Diagnostic Chart* to target your efforts so that you can work most effectively to pass the test.

Some of the questions will check your skills; some will determine your abilities with the types of questions that you will encounter on the actual GED. In Parts 2 and 3, you will have a chance to review and practice what you need to know to pass the test.

2. Review, pages 12–55

Once you have taken the inventory, you can decide which topics you need to review. You may want to select lessons based on the *Diagnostic Chart* or work through the entire section of the book.

Part 2 of this book consists of 22 skill lessons. Each lesson has two parts:

- Skill Review
- Skill Practice

3. Practice, pages 56–83

Once you feel that you have covered the skills, the next step is to practice answering the types of questions that you will find on the GED Tests.

Part 3 of this book consists of *GED Skill Builder* lessons. These seven lessons will review the types of questions that you will see on the actual test. These lessons have three parts:

- Sample Question and Think It Through
- Guided Practice
- GED Practice

Be sure that you use the hints in this part of the book. They will help you to think like a successful GED test-taker.

Best of luck,
The GED Skill Workbook Team

This pretest will help you learn which skills you know well and which skills you need to work on. Answer all of the questions that you can. Write your work in the space provided. Then check your answers on page 10, and use the diagnostic chart on page 11 to analyze the results.

Algebra Review

Perform the operations as indicated.

1. $(-11) + (-7) =$

2. $13 - 17 =$

3. $-18 - (-6) =$

4. $(+5)(-4) =$

5. $(-7)(-12) =$

6. $\dfrac{-75}{5} =$

7. $\dfrac{-15}{-5} =$

8. $(-3)(-7)(-2) =$

Solve using what you know about powers, roots, and the order of operations. For problem 12, estimate the square root by choosing the two whole numbers that the root must come between.

9. $(-3)^3 =$

10. $4^4 =$

11. $\sqrt{49}$

12. $\sqrt{73}$ is between _____ and _____.

13. $\dfrac{54}{(6-3)^2}$

14. $(7-4)(-4+3^2) =$

For problems 15 and 16, write the numbers using scientific notation. For problems 17 and 18, change from scientific notation to <u>standard notation</u>.

15. 15,000

16. 0.00082

17. 5.1×10^3

18. 7.25×10^{-3}

Solve each problem. Then choose the best answer.

19. Which expression multiplies the sum of –4 and 6 by 3?

(1) $3 - (-4 + 6)$
(2) $3(-4 - 6)$
(3) $(-4 + 6) \div 3$
(4) $3(-4 + 6)$
(5) $(-4)(6)(3)$

20. In the following expression, which operation should you perform first?

$2 - 4 - (-3)(5)$

(1) multiply -3 by 5
(2) subtract 4
(3) add 3
(4) subtract 4 from 2
(5) subtract -3

Find the value of each expression when $x = 2$ and $y = -1$.

21. $8x - 3y$

23. $(x - y)(x + y)$

22. $\dfrac{(xy)^2}{-x^2}$

24. $12x + y^3$

Solve for the unknown variable.

25. $x + 8 = 20$

29. $2x + 7 = 25$

26. $4y = 16$

30. $\dfrac{y}{8} - 1 = 4$

27. $\dfrac{a}{6} = -3$

31. $-7z - 5 = -47$

28. $-10x = -100$

32. $3y + 9 = -11 - y$

Solve each problem. Then choose the best answer.

33. Amy pays $30 per month for cell phone service. If she also pays a yearly service fee of $25, how much does Amy pay a year for cell phone service?

    (1) $25
    (2) $30
    (3) $300
    (4) $360
    (5) $385

34. Carl is twice as old as Rita. Meg is 5 years older than Carl. If their combined age is 155 years, how old is Meg?

    (1) 30
    (2) 31
    (3) 60
    (4) 65
    (5) Not enough information is given.

Write the coordinates for each given point on the coordinate plane below.

35. Point A (_____, _____)

36. Point B (_____, _____)

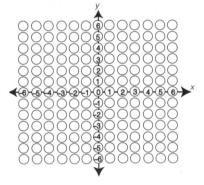

Plot the given points on the blank coordinate plane below.

37. Point G at (−1, 2)

38. Point H at (0, 3)

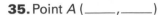

Answer the questions below.

39. Point A is 3 units directly below (2, 2). What are the coordinates of point A?

Point A (_____, _____)

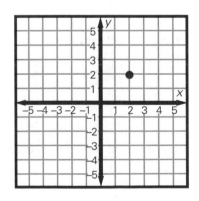

Question 40 is based on the following figure.

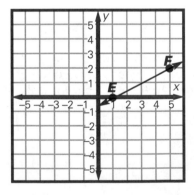

40. What is the slope of the line that passes through points E and F?

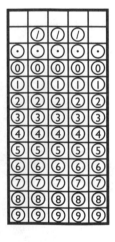

Mark your answers in the circles in the grid.

Solve each inequality.

41. $x - 3 \geq 10$

42. $y + 1 < 6$

43. $-5b - 5 > 5$

44. $10 - \frac{w}{3} \geq 3$

Complete the table of values for each equation. Then write three coordinate pairs.

45. $y = 2x$

x	y
−2	
0	
+2	

Coordinate pairs: (____ , ____)

(____ , ____)

(____ , ____)

46. $y = -x + 1$

x	y
−3	
0	
+3	

Coordinate pairs: (____ , ____)

(____ , ____)

(____ , ____)

Choose the best answer.

47. Which inequality is graphed on the number line below?

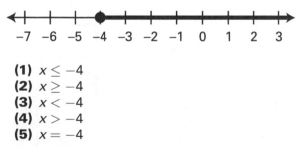

(1) $x \leq -4$
(2) $x \geq -4$
(3) $x < -4$
(4) $x > -4$
(5) $x = -4$

48. Chris wants to save at least $125 per month to pay for a computer. If *w* is the amount he wants to save, which inequality represents his monthly goal?

(1) $w \leq \$125$
(2) $w < \$125$
(3) $w \geq \$125$
(4) $w > \$125$
(5) $w = \$125$

49. A point located at (0, 5) lies on the graph for which of the following linear equations?

(1) $y = 3x - 4$
(2) $y = 2x + 5$
(3) $y = 4x + 9$
(4) $y = -x + 6$
(5) $y = x - 6$

50. A point located at (6, 0) lies on the graph for which of the following linear equations?

(1) $y = 3x - 4$
(2) $y = 2x + 5$
(3) $y = 4x + 9$
(4) $y = x + 6$
(5) $y = x - 6$

Write the number that comes next in each sequence.

51. 6, 3, 0, –3, _____

52. 2, 7, 12, 17, _____

Study the relationship between the numbers and the position in the sequence. Then write a function to determine the missing number.

53.

POSITION (*p*)	1ST	2ND	3RD	4TH	5TH	. . .	10TH
NUMBER (*n*)	2	6	10	14	18	. . .	?

Function: _____   Missing Number: _____

Solve the quadratic equations by solving for *x*. The equations have been factored for you.

54. $x^2 + 5x - 14 = 0$

$(x - 2)(x + 7) = 0$

55. $x^2 - x - 12 = 0$

$(x + 3)(x - 4) = 0$

Solve each problem. Then choose the best answer.

56. In the quadratic equation $2x^2 - 8x = 10$, what is one possible value of *x*?

(1) −5
(2) −1
(3) 1
(4) 2
(5) 3

57. What are the two solutions of the quadratic equation $x^2 - 3x - 54$?

(1) −2 and 27
(2) −9 and 6
(3) −6 and −9
(4) −6 and 9
(5) −18 and 3

58. The total of three consecutive numbers is 84. What is the first, or least, number of the three numbers?

(1) 27
(2) 28
(3) 29
(4) 30
(5) 31

59. The total of three odd consecutive numbers is 27. What is the greatest of the three numbers?

Mark your answers in the circles in the grid.

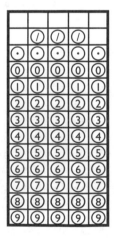

Measurement and Geometry Review

For each angle measure, write the measure of its complementary and supplementary angles.

60. 45°

Complementary angle: _____

Supplementary angle: _____

61. 25°

Complementary angle: _____

Supplementary angle: _____

Answer the following questions based on the art provided.

<u>Questions 62 and 63</u> refer to the following figure.

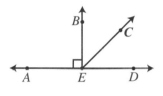

62. What kind of angle is ∠AEB?

    (1) right   **(4)** reflex
    (2) obtuse   **(5)** straight
    (3) acute

63. If ∠AED is a straight angle and ∠BEC measures 30°, what is the measure of ∠CED?

    (1) 30°   **(4)** 120°
    (2) 60°   **(5)** 150°
    (3) 90°

64. In the figure below, lines *e* and *f* are parallel, and $m\angle 2 = 40°$. Fill in the missing measurements.

    a. $m\angle 4 =$ _____
    b. $m\angle 1 =$ _____
    c. $m\angle 6 =$ _____

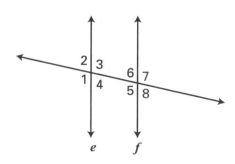

65. In the figure below, ∠AFE is a straight angle. What angle is supplementary to ∠AFB?

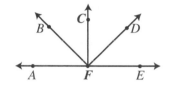

    (1) ∠AFE
    (2) ∠BFC
    (3) ∠BFD
    (4) ∠BFE
    (5) Not enough information is given.

66. What do you know about ∠5 and ∠7?

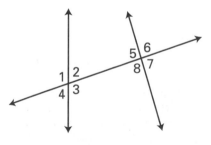

    (1) The angles are adjacent.
    (2) The angles are supplementary.
    (3) The angles are congruent.
    (4) The angles are right angles.
    (5) The angles are complementary.

Write the name of the figure being described.

67. A three-sided figure has three angles, one measuring 90°. _____

68. A four-sided figure has four angles which measure 90°. Two sides measure 6 inches and two sides measure 10 inches. _____

Find the circumference and area of the circle. Find the volume of the cylinder.

69.

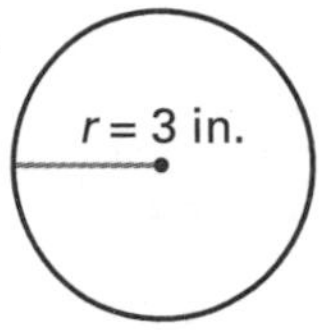

$r = 3$ in.

Circumference _____

Area _____

70.

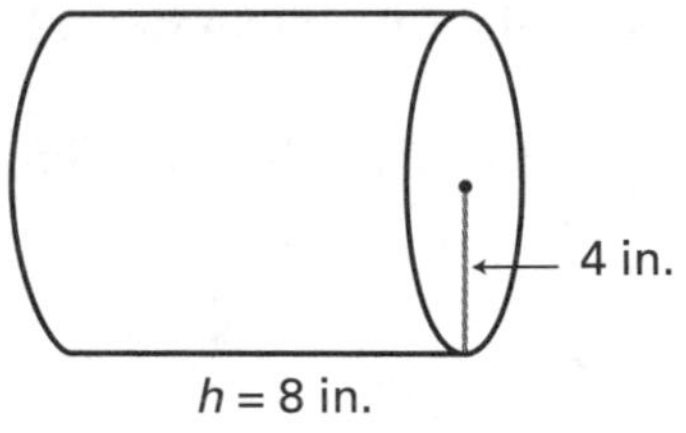

4 in.

$h = 8$ in.

Volume _____

Each problem shows the measures of three sides of a triangle. Decide whether or not the sides form a right triangle. Check *Yes* or *No*.

71. $a = 3$

$b = 4$

$c = 5$

Yes _____ No _____

72. $a = 2$

$b = 2$

$c = 3$

Yes _____ No _____

Solve each problem. Then choose the best answer.

73. A triangle has three angles that each measure 60°. One side of the triangle measures 15 centimeters. Which of the following expressions could be used to find the perimeter of the triangle?

(1) 60×3
(2) 15×3
(3) $60 + 60 + 15$
(4) $15 + 15 + 60$
(5) 15×60

74. If the circumference (C) of a circle is known, which of the following formulas could be used to find the radius of the circle?

(1) $r = \dfrac{C\pi}{2}$

(2) $r = \dfrac{C}{2}$

(3) $r = \dfrac{C}{\pi}$

(4) $r = 2 \times \dfrac{C}{\pi}$

(5) $r = \dfrac{C}{2\pi}$

Find the perimeter of each figure below.

75.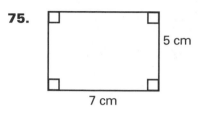

5 cm

7 cm

76.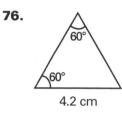

60°

60°

4.2 cm

Find the area of each figure below.

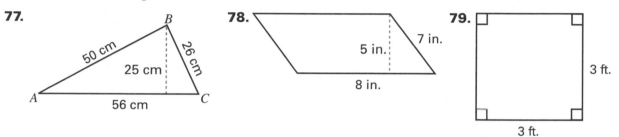

77.

B

50 cm

25 cm

26 cm

A

56 cm

C

78.

5 in.

7 in.

8 in.

79.

3 ft.

3 ft.

Find the volume of each figure below.

80.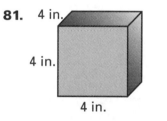

3 m

5 m   7 m

81.   4 in.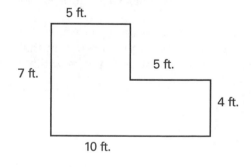

4 in.

4 in.

Solve each problem. Then choose the best answer.

82. A rectangular patio has an area of 104 square meters. If the length is 8 meters, which of these equations could be used to solve for the width (*w*) in meters?

(1) $w = \dfrac{104}{8}$

(2) $w = \dfrac{8}{104}$

(3) $w = 8(104)$

(4) $w = \dfrac{104 - 2(8)}{2}$

(5) $w = 104 - 8$

83. In the drawing, all corners of the room are right angles. Which of the following expressions could be used to find the perimeter, in feet, of the room?

5 ft.

7 ft.

5 ft.

4 ft.

10 ft.

(1) 2(10) + 2(5)
(2) 4(5) + 5(7)
(3) (10)(5)
(4) 10 + 7 + 5 + 5 + 4
(5) 10 + 7 + 5 + 3 + 5 + 4

Find the perimeter and area of each figure below.

84.

2.5 ft.

4 ft.

85.

3 in.   3 in.

2 in.

4 in.

Use your knowledge of congruent and similar figures to answer the questions below.

86.
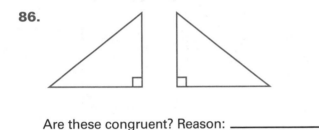

Are these congruent? Reason: _____

_____

88.

Are these similar? Reason: _____

_____

87.
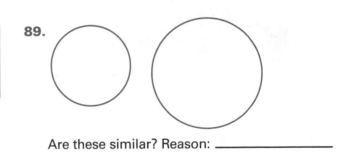

Are these congruent? Reason: _____

_____

89.

Are these similar? Reason: _____

_____

Solve each problem. Then choose the best answer.

90. The length of a rectangle is 2 feet more than twice its width. If the perimeter of the rectangle is 28 feet, what is its width in feet?

   (1) 2
   (2) 4
   (3) 14
   (4) 28
   (5) 40

91. The length of a rectangle is four times its width. If the area is 36 square inches, what is the length of the rectangle?

   (1) 3
   (2) 4
   (3) 9
   (4) 12
   (5) 36

Use your calculator to solve the following problems.

92. What is the value of the expression below when $x = 1$ and $y = -2$?

$$(2x - 5y)(3x + 6y)$$

93. What is the value of $\dfrac{9(-b + 3^2)}{2b + 1}$ if $b = 4$?

94. What is the value of the expression below when $d = 4$ and $e = -6$?

$$\left(\frac{-4d}{-2 - e}\right)^3 + e^2$$

95. What is the value of the expression below when $a = -1$ and $b = 10$?

$$3ab - \sqrt{a + b}$$

96. What is the value of the expression below when $x = -3$?

$$4x^3 + x^2 - 3x + 15$$

97. What is the value of $\dfrac{m + 5}{2(n - 3)}$, when $m = -15$ and $n = 8$?

Solve each problem. Then choose the best answer.

98. Angela has test scores of 82, 88, 78, 85, and 82 in her chemistry class. What is her average test score?

(1) 78
(2) 80
(3) 82
(4) 83
(5) 85

99. Andy rode his bike 12 kilometers due east and then rode 16 kilometers due south. How many kilometers is he from his starting point?

(1) 112
(2) 56
(3) 28
(4) 20
(5) 4

100. Maura borrowed $1,500 for 2 years. At the end of that time, she will owe $1,500 plus $150 in interest. If Maura financed the loan using simple interest, what interest rate did she pay on the loan?

(1) 1%
(2) 5%
(3) 10%
(4) 75%
(5) Not enough information is given.

Answers and explanations start on page 10.

1. –18
2. –4
3. –12
4. –20

5. 84
6. –15
7. 3
8. –42

9. –27
10. 256
11. 7

12. 8 and 9
13. 6
14. 15

15. 1.5×10^4
16. 8.2×10^{-4}

17. 5,100
18. 0.00725

19. (4) 3(–4 + 6)
20. (1) multiply –3 by 5

21. 19
22. 1
23. 3
24. 23
25. $x = 12$
26. $y = 4$

27. $a = -18$
28. $x = 10$
29. $x = 9$
30. $y = 40$
31. $z = 6$
32. $y = -5$

33. (5) $385

34. (4) 65

35. (–3, 3)
36. (4, –1)

37.–38

39. (2, –1)
40. 1/2

41. $x \geq 13$
42. $y < 5$
43. $b < -2$
44. $w \leq 21$
45. (–2, –4) (0, 0) (+2, +4)
46. (–3, +4) (0, +1) (+3, –2)

47. (2) $x \geq -4$
48. (3) $w \geq \$125$

49. (2) $y = 2x + 5$
50. (5) $y = x - 6$

51. –6
52. 22
53. Function: $n = n + 4$
   Missing Number: 38
54. 2 and –7
55. –3 and 4

56. (2) –1
57. (4) –6 and 9
58. (1) 27
59. 11

60. Complementary angle: 45°
   Supplementary angle: 135°
61. Complementary angle: 65°
   Supplementary angle: 155°
62. (1) right
63. (2) 60°
64. a. $m\angle 4 = 40°$
   b. $m\angle 1 = 140°$
   c. $m\angle 6 = 40°$
65. (4) ∠BFE
66. (3) The angles are congruent.

67. Right triangle
68. Rectangle
69. Circumference: 18.84 in.
   Area: 28.26 in.^{2}
70. Volume: 401.92 in.^{3}
71. Yes, the sides form a right triangle because $a^2 + b^2 = c^2$, or $3^2 + 4^2 = 5^2$.
72. No, the sides do not form a right triangle because c^2 does not equal $a^2 + b^2$: $2^2 + 2^2 \neq 3^2$.
73. (2) 15×3
74. (5) $r = \frac{C}{2\pi}$

75. 24 cm
76. 12.6 cm
77. 700 cm^2
78. 40 sq. in.
79. 9 sq. ft.
80. 105 m^3
81. 64 cu. in.
82. (1) $w = \frac{104}{8}$
83. (5) $10 + 7 + 5 + 3 + 5 + 4$

84. $P = 2l + 2w = 2(4) + 2(2.5) = 8 + 5 = 13$ ft.
   $A = lw = 4(2.5) = 10$ sq. ft.
85. $P = s_1 + s_2 + s_3 = 3 + 3 + 4 = 10$ in.
   $A = \frac{1}{2}bh = \frac{1}{2}(4)(2) = 4$ sq. in.
86. Yes, the triangles are congruent because they have the same shape and size.
87. No, the rectangles are not congruent because they have different sizes and proportions.
88. No, the figures are not similar because they have different shapes.
89. Yes, the circles are similar because they have the same shape but are different sizes.
90. (2) 4
91. (4) 12

92. –108
93. 5
94. –28
95. –33
96. –75
97. –1

98. (4) 83
99. (4) 20
100. (2) 5%

Diagnostic Chart

1. Check your answers to the Math Skills Inventory on page 10.
2. Circle the numbers of the questions you got correct.
3. Add the number of questions that you got right for each skill (across), and write the number under Total Correct.
4. Add the number of total questions that you got correct (down).
5. Check off (✓) the skill areas that you feel you most need to work on.

PROBLEM NUMBERS	TOTAL CORRECT	SKILL	✓	PAGE NUMBERS
		Algebra		
1, 2, 3, 4, 5, 6, 7, 8, 19, 20	____ / 10	Integers		pp. 12–13
9, 10, 11, 12, 13, 14	____ / 6	Powers and Roots		pp. 14–15
15, 16, 17, 18	____ / 4	Scientific Notation		pp. 18–19
21, 22, 23, 24	____ / 4	Expressions		pp. 16–17
25, 26, 27, 28	____ / 4	Equations		pp. 20–21
29, 30, 31, 32	____ / 4	Multi-Step Equations		pp. 22–23
35, 36, 37, 38	____ / 4	The Coordinate Plane		pp. 26–27
41, 42, 43, 44, 47, 48	____ / 6	Inequalities		pp. 24–25
45, 46, 49, 50	____ / 4	Linear Equations		pp. 28–29
51, 52, 53	____ / 3	Patterns and Functions		pp. 30–31
54, 55, 56, 57	____ / 4	Quadratic Equations		pp. 32–33
		Measurement and Geometry		
60, 61, 62, 63	____ / 4	Lines and Angles		pp. 34–35
64	____ / 1	Transversals and Parallel Lines		pp. 36–37
67, 68	____ / 2	Triangles and Quadrilaterals		pp. 38–39
69, 70	____ / 2	Circles		pp. 46–47
71, 72	____ / 2	Pythagorean Relationship		pp. 54–55
75, 76	____ / 2	Perimeter		pp. 40–41
77, 78, 79	____ / 3	Area		pp. 42–43
80, 81	____ / 2	Volume		pp. 44–45
84, 85	____ / 2	Irregular Figures		pp. 48–49
86, 87	____ / 2	Congruent Figures		pp. 50–51
88, 89	____ / 2	Similar Figures		pp. 52–53
		GED Questions		
33, 34, 65, 66	____ / 4	Word Problems		pp. 56–59
39	____ / 1	The Coordinate Grid		pp. 76–79
40, 59	____ / 2	The Standard Grid		pp. 72–75
58, 90, 91	____ / 3	Problem Solving		pp. 64–67
73, 74, 82, 83	____ / 4	Formulas and Equations		pp. 60–63
92, 93, 94, 95, 96, 97, 98, 99, 100	____ / 9	The Casio *fx*-260 Calculator		pp. 68–71
TOTAL	____ / 100			

Add and Subtract

A number line can show integers, or signed numbers, continuing in both directions. The sign tells you whether the number is less than or greater than 0. Positive numbers may be shown with or without the + sign.

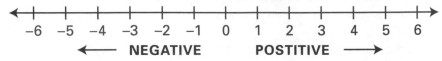

← NEGATIVE   POSTIVE →

When you add integers with the same sign, simply add the numbers and keep the same sign. When integers have different signs, subtract to find the difference, and use the sign from the greater number. In these examples, the parentheses group the sign with each signed number.

$(+5) + (+19) = +24$ $(-17) + (-15) = -32$
$(-6) + (+4) = -2$ $(+13) + (-10) = +3$

Think of subtracting as "adding the opposite." To subtract integers, change the minus sign to a plus sign, and change the sign of the number you are subtracting to its opposite. Then add.

$(+5) - (-12) = (+5) + (+12) = +17$
$(-16) - (+8) = (-16) + (-8) = -24$

Multiply and Divide

In algebra, a multiplication problem is written by writing two integers next to each other in parentheses or by separating two integers with a dot. Division is written as a fraction. The fraction bar means "divided by."

Both $(-5)(+7)$ and $-5 \cdot 7$ mean "negative 5 times positive 7."

$\frac{72}{-9}$ means "positive 72 divided by negative 9."

If you multiply or divide two integers with the same sign, the answer is positive. If they have different signs, the answer is negative.

$(-6)(-11) = +66$ $10 \cdot -5 = -50$ $\frac{-6}{-2} = 3$ $\frac{8}{-1} = -8$

To multiply three integers, multiply two numbers and give them the correct sign. Then multiply by the third number, and change the sign if needed.

$(-8)(-2)(-3) = (16)(-3) = -48$ $(4)(-4)(-2) = (-16)(-2) = 32$

Order of Operations

Some problems require more than one operation. Do the operations in this order. First, work any operations in parentheses. Then do all the multiplying and dividing, working from left to right. Finally, add and subtract, also working from left to right.

parentheses $5(-3 + 7) - \frac{-15}{-3} + (-6) =$

multiply and divide $5(+4) - \frac{15}{-3} + (-6) =$

add and subtract $(+20) - (+5) + (-6) = 9$

Algebra Practice 1

A. Add and subtract as directed.

1. $(+7) + (-13) =$

2. $(-16) + (-9) =$

3. $(-22) + (+30) =$

4. $12 - 15 =$

5. $-14 - (-5) =$

6. $-23 - 8 =$

7. $8 + (-9) - 4 =$

8. $-2 - (-1) + 3 =$

9. $54 - 60 + 6 =$

B. Multiply and divide as directed.

10. $(+3)(-5) =$

11. $(-8)(-10) =$

12. $\dfrac{-60}{4} -$

13. $(7)(-3)(-7) =$

14. $\dfrac{-105}{5} =$

15. $\dfrac{-12}{2} =$

16. $\dfrac{24}{-8} =$

17. $\dfrac{144}{9} =$

18. $(-1)(-5)(-8) =$

C. Solve using the order of operations.

19. $4 - (-3)(+4) =$

20. $(-7) + \dfrac{(-5) + (+9)}{-2} =$

21. $2(-9 - 3) - 18 =$

22. $\dfrac{-6(3 - 5)}{-12 + 15} =$

23. $2 - (-1)(3) =$

24. $(-16 + 12)(2 - 6) =$

25. $-7 - 3(4 - 9) + 15 =$

26. $\dfrac{-2(-5 + 10)}{-10} =$

27. $15 - 22 - \dfrac{14}{-2} =$

D. Solve each problem. Then choose the correct answer.

28. A weather station tracked changes in temperature for a 5-hour period.

TIME	CHANGE IN TEMPERATURE
8–9 A.M.	+6°
9–10 A.M.	+4°
10–11 A.M.	−5°
11 A.M.–Noon	−3°
Noon–1 P.M.	−8°

If it was 48 degrees (°) outside at 8 A.M., what temperature was it at 1 P.M.?

(1) 32°
(2) 38°
(3) 42°
(4) 54°
(5) 58°

29. Which expression subtracts 15 from the sum of −8 and 9?

(1) $15 - (-8 + 9)$
(2) $15 - (-8 - 9)$
(3) $(-8 + 9) - 15$
(4) $(-8 + 9) + 15$
(5) $(-8)(9) - 15$

30. In the following expression, which operation should you perform first?

$$-3 + 4 - 8 - (-9)(2)$$

(1) multiply −9 by 2
(2) subtract 2
(3) add −3
(4) subtract 8 from 4
(5) subtract −9

Answers and explanations start on page 84.

Powers and Exponents

Powers and exponents provide a shorter way of showing repeated multiplication. For instance, suppose you need to show the multiplication of $3 \times 3 \times 3 \times 3$. The number 3 is the base, or the number that is multiplied repeatedly. Since 3 appears in the problem four times, use the exponent 4. An exponent is written as a small raised number next to the base.

$3 \times 3 \times 3 \times 3$ is written 3^4

This process is often called raising a number to a higher power. In the example above, the base of 3 is raised to the fourth power.

To find the value of a power, do the multiplication.

Raise 2 to the fifth power.

$2^5 = 2 \times 2 \times 2 \times 2 \times 2 = 32$

Square Roots

A root is the opposite of a power. On the GED Mathematics Test, you will need to solve problems involving square roots. When a number is squared, it is raised to the second power. In other words, a squared number is multiplied by itself.

"8 squared" is written 8^2, which equals 8×8, or 64.

Square roots are written inside the square root bracket: $\sqrt{\ }$. To find the square root of a number, you need to work backwards. Think: What number multiplied by itself equals this number?

$\sqrt{144} = ?$ What number times itself is 144? $12 \times 12 = 144$

$\sqrt{144} = 12$

You may be asked to estimate the square root of a number.

Estimate the value of $\sqrt{30}$.
Think of the closest square above and below the number.
$5 \times 5 = 25$ and $6 \times 6 = 36$, so $\sqrt{30}$ is **between 5 and 6.**

More About the Order of Operations

Now you can add powers and roots to the order of operations.
1. Do operations inside grouping symbols, which include parentheses, square root brackets, and operations above or below fraction bars.
2. Find the value of any exponents and roots.
3. Multiply and divide, working from left to right.
4. Add and subtract, working from left to right.

grouping symbols $\quad (-4)^2 + \dfrac{21}{6-3} - \sqrt{8+1} =$

exponents and roots $\quad (-4)^2 + \dfrac{21}{3} - \sqrt{9} =$

multiply and divide $\quad 16 + \dfrac{21}{3} - 3 =$

add and subtract $\quad 16 + 7 - 3 = 20$

Algebra Practice 2

A. Find the value of each power or root.

1. $6^2 =$

2. $(-2)^3 =$

3. $3^4 =$

4. $\sqrt{81} =$

5. $\sqrt{121} =$

6. $2^6 =$

7. $(-1)^5 =$

8. $\sqrt{25} =$

9. $4^3 =$

B. Estimate each square root. Write the two whole numbers that the root must come between.

10. $\sqrt{55}$ is between _____ and _____.

11. $\sqrt{112}$ is between _____ and _____.

12. $\sqrt{150}$ is between _____ and _____.

13. $\sqrt{10}$ is between _____ and _____.

C. Solve using the order of operations.

14. $3 \cdot 2^3 - 5 \cdot 4 =$

15. $2(-3 + -2)^2 =$

16. $\dfrac{36}{(5-2)^2} =$

17. $\dfrac{(7 \cdot 2 + -6)}{-1} =$

18. $5^3 - \sqrt{100} =$

19. $(4-10)^2 - (3)(-6) =$

20. $(8-3)(-6 + 4^2) =$

21. $\dfrac{6 + 8^2}{\sqrt{17 + 8}} =$

22. $(3-7)^2 + 2(5-3) =$

D. Solve each problem. Then choose the correct answer.

23. Which of the following expressions is equal to 6^3?

(1) 3^6
(2) $(4+2)(3-9)(1+5)$
(3) $9 \cdot 4 + 6$
(4) $2 \cdot 3^3$
(5) $2(10^2) + 4^2$

24. In the following expression, which operation should you perform first?

$$\frac{3^4 + 9}{2 - 4 \cdot 3}$$

(1) subtract 4 from 2
(2) divide by 2
(3) raise 3 to the fourth power
(4) add 4 and 9
(5) add 3 and 9

25. To find the area (A) of a square, you raise one side (s) of the square to the second power: $A = s^2$. In square inches, what is the total area of the two squares below?

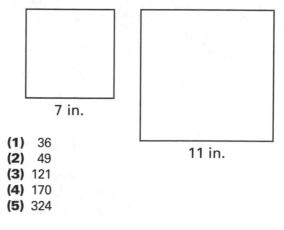

7 in.

11 in.

(1) 36
(2) 49
(3) 121
(4) 170
(5) 324

Answers and explanations start on page 84.

Use of Variables

Variables are used to represent unknown values in expressions. Variables are usually letters of the alphabet. Each time the same letter is used in an expression, it represents the same number. Different letters represent different numbers.

Study these examples to see how words can be translated into algebraic expressions.

3 times a number plus 10	$3x + 10$
9 decreased by 2 times a number	$9 - 2p$
Two times the sum of two different numbers	$2(x + y)$
A number squared less 7	$x^2 - 7$
A number divided by 5	$\frac{n}{5}$

You may find it helpful to review these words and phrases that are often associated with certain operations.

- addition—sum, plus, total, subtotal, combined with
- subtraction—difference, less, decreased by
- multiplication—product, times, doubled, tripled
- division—quotient, divided by, divided equally

Evaluate Expressions

On the GED Mathematics Test, you will be asked to evaluate algebraic expressions. You will be given number values for the variables in the expression. To find the value of the expression, substitute the numbers in place of the variables, and use the order of operations.

Find the value of $6x + 2y$ when $x = -3$ and $y = 4$.

Substitute numbers for the variables.	$6(-3) + 2(4) =$
Multiply.	$-18 + 8 =$
Add.	-10

Algebraic expressions can seem complicated when there are many subtraction symbols or negative numbers. For instance, what is the value of $-x$, if x is equal to -2? Substitute for the variable: $-x = -(-2)$. What is the value of $-(-2)$? When two negative signs are next to each other, change them to a positive: $-(-2) = +2$.

What is the value of the expression below when $m = -6$ and $n = -5$?

$$-2m - (3n - m) + n^2$$

Substitute for the variables.	$-2(-6) - [(3)(-5) - (-6)] + (-5)^2 =$
Group symbols.	$-2(-6) - [-15 - (-6)] + (-5)^2 =$
	$-2(-6) - [-15 + 6] + (-5)^2 =$
Simplify exponents.	$-2(-6) - (-9) + (-5)^2 =$
Multiply.	$-2(-6) - (-9) + 25 =$
Add and subtract.	$12 - (-9) + 25 =$
	$12 + 9 + 25 = \mathbf{46}$

Algebra Practice 3

A. Match each description in column A to the algebraic expression in column B.

Column A		Column B
1. _____	four times the sum of a number and seven	**A.** $4x + 7$
2. _____	seven more than four times a number	**B.** $4x - 7$
3. _____	the product of four and a number decreased by seven	**C.** $\dfrac{4 - x}{7}$
4. _____	a number raised to the fourth power increased by seven	**D.** $4(x + 7)$
5. _____		**E.** $x^4 + 7$
	the difference of four and a number divided by seven	

B. Find the value of each expression when $x = 3$ and $y = -2$. Note: Use brackets [ ] to avoid double parentheses when needed. (See problem 8 that is started for you.)

6. $8x - 3y$

7. $\dfrac{-5xy}{6}$

8. $4x - (2xy - 7y) = 4(3) - [2(3)(-2) - 7(-2)] =$

9. $9x^2 + y - 25$

10. $\dfrac{(xy)^2}{-(x^2)}$

11. $(x - y)(x + y)$

C. Solve each problem. Then choose the correct answer.

12. What is the value of the following expression when $a = -2$ and $b = -4$?

$5(4a - 3b) + ab$

- **(1)** -108
- **(2)** -92
- **(3)** -12
- **(4)** 12
- **(5)** 28

13. Anya earns $150 less than three times Rick's monthly salary. If Rick's salary is represented by x, which expression represents Anya's salary?

- **(1)** $x - 3 \cdot \$150$
- **(2)** $3(x + \$150)$
- **(3)** $3(x - \$150)$
- **(4)** $3x - \$150$
- **(5)** $3x + \$150$

14. Box A holds 2.5 pounds more than twice the weight of Box B. Let x represent the weight of Box B. Which expression represents the weight of Box A?

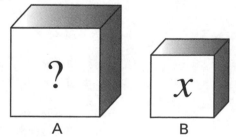

- **(1)** $2.5x + 2$
- **(2)** $2x + 2.5$
- **(3)** $2(x + 2.5)$
- **(4)** $2.5(x + 2)$
- **(5)** $x + 2(2.5)$

Answers and explanations start on page 84.

Write Large Numbers in Scientific Notation

Scientific notation makes it easy to write very small or large numbers. In scientific notation, a number is written as a power of ten multiplied by a number between 1 and 10.

5,800 can be written as 5.8×10^3
$10^3 = 1,000$, so $5.8 \times 1,000 = 5,800$

To change a large number to scientific notation, follow these steps:
1. Move the decimal point left until you get a whole number between 1 and 10.
2. Count how many places you moved the decimal point. The number of places you moved the decimal point becomes the exponent.

Write 3,560,000 in scientific notation.
● Move the decimal point left until you get a number between 1 and 10.
● You moved the decimal point 6 places, so the number is written **3.56×10^6.**

Write Small Numbers in Scientific Notation

To change a small number to scientific notation, follow these steps:
1. Move the decimal point to the right until you get a whole number between 1 and 10.
2. Count the number of places you moved the decimal point. Write the exponent as a negative number.

Write 0.00000064 in scientific notation.
● Move the decimal point to the right, stopping after the 6.
● You moved the decimal point 7 places, so the number is written **6.4×10^{-7}.**

Write Scientific Notation in Standard Notation

To change from scientific notation to standard notation, work backwards.
● If the power of ten is a positive number, move the decimal point that many places to the right, adding zeros as necessary.
● If the power of ten is a negative number, move the decimal point that many places to the left, adding zeros as necessary.

$8.25 \times 10^5 = ?$ Move the decimal point five places to the right: 825000.
$8.25 \times 10^5 = $ **825,000**

$1.9 \times 10^{-4} = ?$ Move the decimal point four places to the left: .00019
$1.9 \times 10^{-4} = $ **0.00019**

Notice that a zero was put in the ones place in the answer of the last example. The zero makes it clear that this number doesn't have a whole number part. This zero doesn't affect the size of the number.

You will need to understand scientific notation to use a scientific calculator. When an answer has more digits than the calculator can display, it shows the answer in scientific notation.

The display $\boxed{1.6\ ^8}$ means 1.6×10^8.
The display $\boxed{6.25\ ^{-3}}$ means 6.25×10^{-3}.

Algebra Practice 4

A. Write the following numbers in scientific notation.

1. 13,000

3. 5,600,000

5. 0.00000000852

2. 6,150,000,000

4. 0.00078

6. 0.00000073

B. Change from scientific notation to standard notation.

7. 1.5×10^3

9. 8.0×10^8

11. 1.75×10^{-3}

8. 2.67×10^5

10. 4.9×10^{-5}

12. 2.8×10^{-9}

C. Solve each problem. Then choose the correct answer.

13. A filament is 0.000058 millimeter wide. How would you express the width of the wire in scientific notation?

(1) 58×10^{-4}
(2) 5.8×10^{-5}
(3) 58×10^{-6}
(4) 5.8×10^{-6}
(5) 5.8×10^6

14. Scientists estimate that the dinosaurs became extinct 65 million years ago. How would this length of time be written in scientific notation?

(1) 6.5×10^7
(2) 6.5×10^6
(3) 6.5×10^5
(4) 65×10^6
(5) 65×10^5

15. The chart below shows the diameter of five planets in our solar system.

PLANET	DIAMETER (IN MILES)
Earth	7.9×10^3
Mars	4.2×10^3
Jupiter	8.8×10^4
Saturn	7.5×10^4
Neptune	3.1×10^4
Pluto	1.4×10^3

Of the planets in the chart, Earth's diameter is closest to which of the other planets' diameters?

(1) Mars
(2) Jupiter
(3) Saturn
(4) Neptune
(5) Pluto

Answers and explanations start on page 84.

Solve for the Unknown

An equation is a mathematical statement that two expressions are equal. For example: $9 + 14 = 23$. The equals sign (=) is like the center point of a balance scale. Everything on the left of the sign must balance with everything on the right.

In algebra, one or both sides of an equation may contain a variable. To solve an equation, you want to isolate the variable. In other words, you want the variable to be on one side of the equals sign and a number value to be on the other side.

Use inverse, or opposite, operations to isolate the variable. Addition and subtraction are opposites, and multiplication and division are opposites. Study the examples below to see how to use inverse operations.

$x + 5 = 13$	5 is being added to x.
$x + 5 - 5 = 13 - 5$	Subtract 5 from both sides.
$x = 8$	

$25 = x - 9$	9 is being subtracted from x.
$25 + 9 = x - 9 + 9$	Add 9 to both sides.
$34 = x$	Notice x can be isolated on either side.

$4x = -24$	x is being multiplied by 4.
$\frac{4x}{4} = \frac{-24}{4}$	Divide both sides by 4.
$x = -6$	

$\frac{x}{3} = 12$	x is being divided by 3.
$3 \times \frac{x}{3} = 3 \times 12$	Multiply both sides by 3.
$x = 36$	

Simple Word Problems

To solve algebra word problems, you must translate the information into an equation. Assign a variable to the unknown number in the problem. Then use inverse operations to find the value of the variable.

The difference between a number and -4 is 14. What is the number?

Let x represent the unknown number.	
Write an equation.	$x - (-4) = 14$
Simplify.	$x + 4 = 14$
Subtract 4 from both sides.	$x + 4 - 4 = 14 - 4$
Solve.	$x = 10$

Check your work by substituting your answer into the original equation.

Substitute.	$10 - (-4) = 14$
Simplify.	$10 + 4 = 14$
Solve.	$14 = 14$

Since both sides are equal, the solution is correct.

Algebra Practice 5

A. Solve each equation using inverse operations. Check your work by substituting your answer into the original equation.

1. $x + 7 = 19$

2. $3y = 15$

3. $\frac{a}{4} = -2$

4. $w - 10 = 21$

5. $-11x = -110$

6. $13 + s = 6$

7. $\frac{t}{-5} = 20$

8. $12 - y = -4$

9. $4z = -36$

10. $8 + p = -9$

B. Solve each problem. Then choose the correct answer.

11. On weekends Mike earns \$15 per hour, or 1.5 times his regular wage. Which of the equations below could be used to find Mike's regular hourly wage (w)?

(1) $\$15w = 1.5$

(2) $1.5w = \$15$

(3) $\frac{1.5}{w} = \$15$

(4) $\frac{w}{1.5} = \$15$

(5) $\$15 - w = 1.5$

12. Kendra went on a 2-day road trip. She drove 45 miles farther on the second day than she did on the first. If she drove 355 miles on the second day, how far did she drive on the first day?

(1) 43
(2) 90
(3) 160
(4) 200
(5) 310

13. Which of these numbers makes the following equation true?
$$\frac{-16}{n} = 32$$

(1) -512
(2) -2
(3) -0.5
(4) 0.5
(5) 2

14. The drawing below shows the front of the Grahams' property.

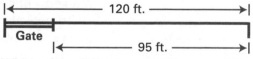

Which of the following equations could be used to find the length (L), in feet, of the gate?

(1) $95 + L = 120$
(2) $120 + L = 95$
(3) $95 - L = 120$
(4) $120L = 95$
(5) $95L = 120$

Answers and explanations start on page 84.

Combine Like Terms

Most algebra problems require more than one step, but the goal is the same. You need to isolate the variable on one side of the equation.

When an equation has many terms, you will need to combine like terms to solve it. Integers are like terms. Like terms also include terms that have the same combination of variables. For example, $5x$ and $8x$ are like terms because both have the variable x. The terms $3y$ and $3x$ are unlike terms because the variables are different.

Use these steps to solve multi-step equations.
1. Combine like terms on both sides of the equation.
2. Use inverse operations to get all the variables on one side.
3. Perform the inverse of any addition and subtraction operations.
4. Perform the inverse of any multiplication and division operations.

Solve for x.

$$4 - 3x + 9 = 6x - 7 + x$$

$$4 - 3x + 9 = 6x - 7 + x$$

Combine like terms. $\quad\quad 13 - 3x = 7x - 7$

Add $3x$ to both sides. $\quad 13 - 3x + 3x = 7x + 3x - 7$

$$13 = 10x - 7$$

Add 7 to both sides. $\quad\quad 13 + 7 = 10x - 7 + 7$

$$20 = 10x$$

Divide both sides by 10. $\quad\quad \dfrac{20}{10} = \dfrac{10x}{10}$

$$\mathbf{2} = x$$

You can check your answer by substituting it for the variable into the original problem.

Word Problems

Many word problems can be solved by writing an equation. Use a variable to represent one of the numbers in the problem. Then use algebraic language to express the rest of the information in relation to that variable.

Mary is 4 years older than 3 times Brian's age. The total of their ages is 56 years. How old is Mary?

If x represents Brian's age, Mary is $3x + 4$ years old.
You know Brian's age plus Mary's age is 56 years.

Write an equation. $\quad\quad\quad x + 3x + 4 = 56$

$$4x + 4 = 56$$

$$4x + 4 - 4 = 56 - 4$$

$$4x = 52$$

$$\dfrac{4x}{4} = \dfrac{52}{4}$$

Solve. (Note that $x = 1x$.) $\quad\quad x = 13$

You know that Brian's age (represented by x) is 13, but how old is Mary?
Substitute 13 for x: $3(13) + 4 = 43$. **Mary is 43 years old.**

Algebra Practice 6

A. **Solve each equation. Check your work by substituting your answer into the original equation.**

1. $2x + 7 = 11$

2. $\dfrac{y}{6} - 4 = 6$

3. $5 - 10t = -25$

4. $8 + \dfrac{w}{7} = 6$

5. $6s - 5 = -35$

6. $-9z - 4 = -58$

7. $\dfrac{x}{11} + 15 = 18$

8. $2y + 16 = -11 - y$

9. $14 - 2p = -10 + 6p$

10. $\dfrac{z}{4} = -13 - 3z$

B. **Solve each problem. Then choose the correct answer.**

11. A number (n) is equal to 60 decreased by 3 times the number. What is the value of n?

  (1) 180
  (2) 57
  (3) 23
  (4) 17
  (5) 15

12. 28 is equal to 4 more than 3 times a number. What is the number?

  (1) 7
  (2) 8
  (3) 10
  (4) 16
  (5) 40

13. A soccer league had 120 children sign up. Twenty more girls than boys signed up. Let x equal the number of boys who signed up. Which equation could be used to solve for the number of boys?

  (1) $x + x = 120$
  (2) $2x = 120$
  (3) $x + (x + 20) = 120$
  (4) $120 - x = x + 20$
  (5) $x + 20x = 120$

14. The driving distance between three cities is shown on the map below.

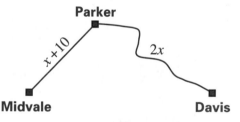

The total distance from Midvale to Parker to Davis is 220 miles. How far is it from Parker to Davis?

  (1) 70
  (2) 80
  (3) 100
  (4) 105
  (5) 140

Answers and explanations start on page 85.

Solve Inequalities

An inequality is a mathematical statement that two sides are not equal. Instead of an equals sign, inequalities use the following symbols:

$<$	less than	$\leq$	less than or equal to
$>$	greater than	$\geq$	greater than or equal to

Solving an inequality is much like solving an equation. Follow the steps for solving an equation, but use the inequality symbol instead.

Solve for x.

$$3x - 9 < 12 \qquad \text{Add 9 to both sides.}$$
$$3x < 21 \qquad \text{Divide both sides by 3.}$$
$$\boldsymbol{x < 7}$$

The answer to an inequality represents a range of answers. In the example above, the answer is read "x is less than 7," which means that any value that is less than 7 will make the inequality true.

The only difference in solving inequalities comes when you multiply or divide by a negative number. Each time this happens, you have to reverse the inequality symbol so that it points the other way.

Solve for y.

$$-2y + 3 \geq 6y - 29 \qquad \text{Subtract } 6y \text{ from both sides.}$$
$$-8y + 3 \geq -29 \qquad \text{Subtract 3 from both sides.}$$
$$-8y \geq -32 \qquad \text{Divide both sides by } -8, \text{ and}$$
$$\boldsymbol{y \leq 4} \qquad \text{reverse the inequality sign.}$$
$$\qquad y \text{ is less than or equal to 4}$$

Remember, only reverse the inequality sign when you multiply or divide both sides by a negative number. Don't reverse the sign if you are adding or subtracting a negative number. You may need to reverse the sign more than once during the same problem.

Graph Inequalities

Graphs are often used to make the answer to an inequality easier to picture. The graph is shown on a number line. An open circle marks the number in the answer, and the side of the number line that represents the answer is darkened. Study these examples.

Graph $a < -2$.

Graph $b > 4$.

When an inequality uses either $\leq$ or $\geq$, the circle over the number is filled in to show that the number in the circle is included in the answer.

Graph $c \geq -3$.

Graph $d \leq 5$.

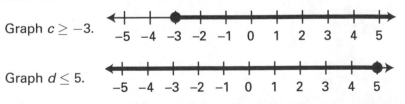

Algebra Practice 7

A. Solve each inequality.

1. $x - 6 \geq 13$

2. $y + 4 < 3$

3. $3z + 7 \leq 28$

4. $-6b - 15 > 9$

5. $\dfrac{n}{2} + 15 < 25$

6. $16 - \dfrac{w}{9} + 4 \geq 9$

B. Solve each inequality, and graph the solution on the number line.

7. $5x \leq 20$

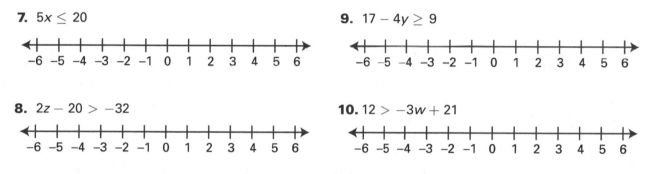

8. $2z - 20 > -32$

9. $17 - 4y \geq 9$

10. $12 > -3w + 21$

C. Solve each problem. Then choose the correct answer.

11. Which inequality is graphed on the number line below?

(1) $x \leq -4$
(2) $x \geq -4$
(3) $x < -4$
(4) $x > -4$
(5) $x = -4$

12. Matt needs to save at least $150 per month to pay for his wedding. If w is the amount he needs to save, which inequality represents his monthly goal?

(1) $w \leq \$150$
(2) $w \geq \$150$
(3) $w < \$150$
(4) $w > \$150$
(5) $w = \$150$

13. Three times a number (n) less 4 is greater than or equal to -13. What is the solution?

(1) $n \leq -3$
(2) $n \geq -3$
(3) $n \leq 3$
(4) $n \geq 3$
(5) $n > 3$

14. Which of the following could be a solution for the inequality $x + 4 < 9$?

(1) 14
(2) 13
(3) 9
(4) 5
(5) 4

Answers and explanations start on page 85.

Understand the Coordinate Plane

Imagine you are looking at a road map spread out on a table. How could you describe the exact location of a town on the map? One way would be to explain how far and in what direction the town is from another landmark on the map.

A coordinate plane is much the same. A line (the *y*-axis) is drawn through the center of the plane from top to bottom, and another line (the *x*-axis) is drawn through the center from left to right. The point where the two lines intersect is called the origin. The two axis lines are marked in regular intervals like number lines. Both have zero at the origin.

We can use the labels on the coordinate plane to name the specific location of any point on the plane. To do this, we describe how far and in what direction the point is from the origin.

Locate and Plot Points

The address of a point on the coordinate plane is given by naming two numbers: the *x*-coordinate and the *y*-coordinate. The *x*-coordinate, the first number, tells where the point is located in relation to the horizontal number line, or *x*-axis. The *y*-coordinate is written second. It tells where the point is located in relation to the vertical number line, or *y*-axis.

What are the coordinates of point *A* on the coordinate plane shown at the right?
1. Move right along the *x*-axis. The point lines up with +3 on the *x*-axis. (3,)
2. Move down along the *y*-axis. The point lines up with −2 on the *y*-axis. (, −2)
3. The coordinates of point *A* are **(3, −2).**

Plot point *B* with the coordinates (−4, 5) on the coordinate plane at the right.
1. Move your pencil point to −4 on the *x*-axis.
2. Move up from −4 until you are across from +5 on the *y*-axis.
3. Mark the point on the coordinate plane.

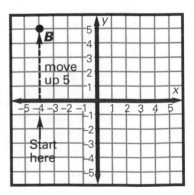

Algebra Practice 8

A. Write the coordinates for each given point on the coordinate plane below.

1. Point A (_____, _____)

2. Point B (_____, _____)

3. Point C (_____, _____)

4. Point D (_____, _____)

5. Point E (_____, _____)

6. Point F (_____, _____)

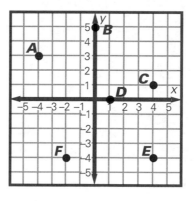

B. Plot the given points on the coordinate plane below.

7. Point G at $(-2, 3)$

8. Point H at $(0, 4)$

9. Point J at $(3, -1)$

10. Point K at $(-4, -4)$

11. Point L at $(-3, 0)$

12. Point M at $(1, 3)$

C. Solve each problem. Then choose the correct answer.

13. On a coordinate plane, point A is located at $(3, -1)$. If point B is 3 units above and 4 units to the left of point A, what are the coordinates of point B?

  (1) $(6, -5)$ **(4)** $(-1, 2)$
  (2) $(6, -4)$ **(5)** $(-1, 7)$
  (3) $(0, -5)$

14. Which of the following points is located at $(-2, 1)$ on the coordinate plane?

  (1) P
  (2) Q
  (3) R
  (4) S
  (5) T

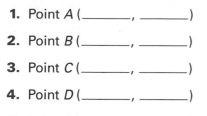

15. Without plotting the point $(5, 5)$, what do you know about the placement of this point?

  It is located

  (1) at the origin
  (2) in the upper-right section of the plane
  (3) in the lower-right section of the plane
  (4) in the upper-left section of the plane
  (5) in the lower-left section of the plane

16. What is the y-coordinate of the point shown below?

  (1) -2
  (2) -1
  (3) 0
  (4) 1
  (5) 2

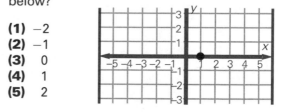

Answers and explanations start on page 85.

Equations with Two Variables

Some equations have two variables, usually *x* and *y*. There are an infinite number of solution pairs for an equation with two variables. Think about the example $y = 2x - 5$. Each time the value of *x* changes, the value of *y* changes. Any of the solutions can be written as a coordinate pair in the order (x, y).

Let *x* = 1.

$$y = 2x - 5$$
$$= 2(1) - 5$$
$$= 2 - 5$$
$$= -3$$

Let *x* = 2.

$$y = 2x - 5$$
$$= 2(2) - 5$$
$$= 4 - 5$$
$$= -1$$

Let *x* = 3.

$$y = 2x - 5$$
$$= 2(3) - 5$$
$$= 6 - 5$$
$$= 1$$

These solutions would be written as **(1, −3)**, **(2, −1)**, and **(3, 1)**.

Graph Linear Equations

The solutions to $y = 2x - 5$ can be plotted on a coordinate plane. Notice that you can draw a line through the three points. The line itself is a graph of all the possible solutions to the equation.

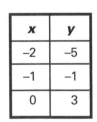

The points shown on the graph for $y = 2x - 5$ are (1, –3), (2, –1), and (3, 1).

To solve an equation with two variables, make a table of coordinate pairs. Choose at least three different values for either *x* or *y*, and then solve for the other variable. Choose values that are easy to work with.

Graph the equation $y - 4x = 3$.

1. Rewrite the equation so that one variable is alone on one side of the equals sign.
   $y - 4x = 3$ can be rewritten as $y = 3 + 4x$.
2. Substitute values of –2, –1, and 0 for *x*. Solve for *y*. Fill in a table of values.
3. Plot the points on the coordinate plane.
4. Draw a line through the plotted points.

x	y
–2	–5
–1	–1
0	3

Why choose three points when you can draw a line with only two points? The third point helps you guard against errors. If the three points do not line up, you know you have made a mistake.

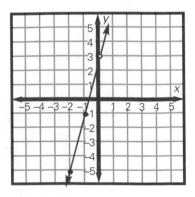

Algebra Practice 9

A. Complete the table of values for each equation. Then write three coordinate pairs.

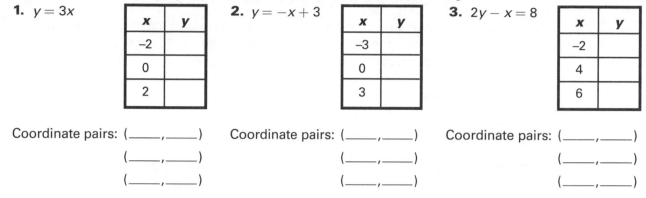

1. $y = 3x$

x	y
−2	
0	
2	

2. $y = -x + 3$

x	y
−3	
0	
3	

3. $2y - x = 8$

x	y
−2	
4	
6	

Coordinate pairs: (____,____)
(____,____)
(____,____)

Coordinate pairs: (____,____)
(____,____)
(____,____)

Coordinate pairs: (____,____)
(____,____)
(____,____)

B. Graph these linear equations on the coordinate plane below.

4. $y = x + 1$

5. $y - x = -4$

6. $3x + 2 = y$

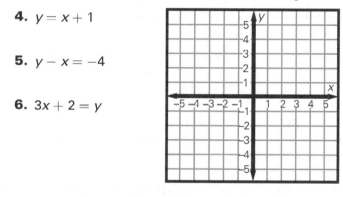

C. Solve each problem. Then choose the correct answer.

Question 7 refers to the coordinate plane below.

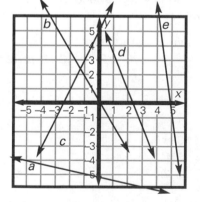

7. Which line is a graph of the linear equation $y = 2x + 5$?

(1) Line *a*   **(4)** Line *d*
(2) Line *b*   **(5)** Line *e*
(3) Line *c*

8. A point located at (−5, 11) lies on the graph for which of the following linear equations?

(1) $y = 3x - 4$
(2) $y = 2x + 5$
(3) $y = 4x + 9$
(4) $y = -x + 6$
(5) $y = x - 6$

Answers and explanations start on page 85.

Number Patterns

Each number pattern, or sequence, is defined by a rule. Once you know the rule, you can find what number comes next.

What number comes next in the sequence 2, 6, 10, 14?

Examine the numbers in the sequence. Think: What happens as you go from one number to the next? In this sequence, each number is 4 more than the one before, so add 4 to find the next number: $14 + 4 = $ **18.**

Now suppose you had to predict the 50th number in this sequence. How could you do it? You could keep adding 4 until you reached the 50th number, or you could write a function.

Functions

A function is a rule that is written as an equation. In the example above, think about how the position in the sequence can be used to determine the number.

POSITION (p)	1ST	2ND	3RD	4TH	5TH	. . .	50TH
NUMBER (n)	2	6	10	14	18	. . .	?

What is the 50th number in the sequence?
1. Find the relationship between the position and the number. Each number in the sequence is 2 less than four times its position number.
2. Write the function. Let p represent the position in the sequence and n represent the number itself. The function for finding any number in this sequence can be written $n = 4p - 2$.
3. Substitute 50 for p: $n = 4(50) - 2$, so $n = 200 - 2$, which equals 198. The 50th number in the sequence is **198.**

Functions are used in very practical situations. For instance, mathematicians say that distance is a function of rate and time. In other words, how far you travel depends on how fast you go and how long you travel, or *distance = rate × time.*

A small jet traveled for 2 hours at an average speed of 520 miles per hour. How many miles did the jet travel?

Use the following function: distance $=$ rate $\times$ time
$$= 520 \times 2 = \textbf{1,040 miles}$$

Functions and Graphs

Many functions can be graphed.

David pays $3 per month for long distance plus $0.07 per minute. Let the y-axis represent dollar amounts and the x-axis represent minutes. How much will David spend in a month in which he makes 200 minutes of calls?

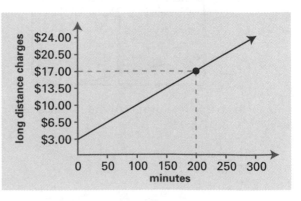

Read the graph. David will pay **$17.**

Algebra Practice 10

A. Figure out the rule, and write the number that comes next in each sequence.

1. 5   2   −1   −4   _____

2. 2   4   8   16   _____

3. $\frac{1}{3}$ $\frac{1}{6}$ $\frac{1}{9}$ $\frac{1}{12}$ _____

4. 0.5   0.25   0.125   _____

5. 3   9   15   21   _____

6. 1   2   3   5   8   _____

B. Study the relationship between the numbers and the position in the sequence. Then write a function to determine the missing number.

7.

POSITION (p)	1ST	2ND	3RD	4TH	5TH	. . .	10TH
NUMBER (n)	4	8	12	16	20	. . .	?

Function: _____   Missing Number: _____

8.

POSITION (p)	1ST	2ND	3RD	4TH	5TH	. . .	25TH
NUMBER (n)	4	7	10	13	16	. . .	?

Function: _____   Missing Number: _____

9.

POSITION (p)	1ST	2ND	3RD	4TH	5TH	. . .	40TH
NUMBER (n)	9	15	21	27	33	. . .	?

Function: _____   Missing Number: _____

C. Solve each problem. Then choose the correct answer.

10. For a business, the cost of mailing a letter is a function of the letter's weight. Using the graph below, how much would it cost to mail a letter that weighs 5.5 ounces?

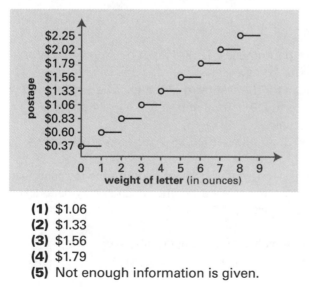

(1) $1.06
(2) $1.33
(3) $1.56
(4) $1.79
(5) Not enough information is given.

11. Bill works as a salesperson. He is paid $400 per month plus 15% of his total sales. Which of the following functions can be used to find his earnings (E) if his total sales (s) are known?

(1) $E = \$400 + s$
(2) $E = \$400s + 0.15s$
(3) $E = \$400s \bullet 0.15$
(4) $E = \$400 + 0.15s$
(5) $E = \$400 + s + 0.15s$

12. The numbers in a series are determined by the function $n = -8p + 5$, where $n =$ a number in the series and $p =$ the position of the number in the series. What is the fourth number in the series?

(1) −37
(2) −32
(3) −27
(4) 27
(5) 37

Answers and explanations start on page 86.

Factor Quadratic Equations

A quadratic equation takes the form $ax^2 + bx + c = 0$. The letters a, b, and c represent numbers. The variables in the equation are x^2 and x (although other letters can be used). Most quadratic equations have two solutions. There are several methods for finding these solutions, but for the GED Mathematics Test, you will only need to learn about factoring.

The factors of a quadratic equation each have two terms written in parentheses; for example, $x^2 + 2x - 15$ equals the factors $(x + 5)(x - 3)$. See how the factors are used to solve the equation $x^2 + 2x - 15 = 0$.

The factors are $(x + 5)$ and $(x - 3)$. Set each factor equal to 0 and solve for x.

$x + 5 = 0$ $x - 3 = 0$
$x = -5$ $x = 3$

The two answers to the equation $x^2 + 2x - 15 = 0$ are **−5 and 3.**

To multiply factors with more than one term, use the distributive property to multiply each term in the first expression by each term in the second expression. Then combine like terms.

Multiply: $(x + 5)(x - 3)$

The FOIL method can help you remember how to organize your work.

First terms	$(x + 5)(x - 3)$	$x \bullet x = x^2$
Outer terms	$(x + 5)(x - 3)$	$x \bullet -3 = -3x$
Inner terms	$(x + 5)(x - 3)$	$5 \bullet x = 5x$
Last terms	$(x + 5)(x - 3)$	$5 \bullet -3 = -15$
Combine terms:	$x^2 + (-3x) + 5x + (-15) = \mathbf{x^2 + 2x - 15}$	

Learning to factor quadratic expressions takes a lot of practice. The only way to do it is to work backwards and use logic. The steps below can help. See how they apply to solving this example.

Factor: $x^2 + 10x + 24$

1. Create two sets of parentheses: (   )(   )
2. Factor the first term: $(x$ $)(x$ $)$
3. Think of two factors for the last term (24) that, when combined, will equal the middle term (10x). Try 6 and 4: $6 \times 4 = 24$ and $6 + 4 = 10$.
4. Fill in the parentheses: $(x + 4)(x + 6)$
5. Use FOIL to check: $(x + 4)(x + 6) = x^2 + 6x + 4x + 24 = x^2 + 10x + 24$

Use Guess and Check

On the GED Mathematics Test, you won't have a lot of time to spend factoring expressions, so the best way to solve a quadratic equation may be to test each of the answer choices in the equation.

What is the one possible value of x in the equation $x^2 - 5x = -4$?

    (1) −4   **(2)** −1   **(3)** 0   **(4)** 2   **(5)** 4

Try each choice in the equation. Only **(5) 4** makes the equation true.

Algebra Practice 11

A. Use FOIL to multiply the factors.

1. $(x + 7)(x + 3)$

3. $(2x + 5)(x - 1)$

2. $(x - 4)(x + 9)$

4. $(x - 12)(x - 8)$

B. Solve the quadratic equations. The equations have been factored for you. Remember to set each factor equal to 0 and solve for x.

5.
$$x^2 - x - 30 = 0$$
$$(x - 6)(x + 5) = 0$$

7.
$$x^2 + 9x + 14 = 0$$
$$(x + 7)(x + 2) = 0$$

6.
$$x^2 - 4x + 3 = 0$$
$$(x - 3)(x - 1) = 0$$

8.
$$x^2 - 5x - 24 = 0$$
$$(x + 3)(x - 8) = 0$$

C. Solve each problem. Then choose the correct answer.

9. In the quadratic equation $3x^2 - 2x = 8$, what is one possible value of x?

(1) −4
(2) −2
(3) 2
(4) 3
(5) 4

10. Which of the following is one of the factors of the quadratic expression $x^2 - 13x + 40$?

(1) $(x + 5)$
(2) $(x + 8)$
(3) $(x - 4)$
(4) $(x - 5)$
(5) $(x - 10)$

11. What are the two solutions of the quadratic equation $x^2 - 8x - 48$?

(1) −4 and 12
(2) −2 and 24
(3) −6 and −8
(4) −8 and 6
(5) −12 and 4

12. The factors $(x + 2)$ and $(x - 1)$ are the factors of what quadratic expression?

(1) $x^2 - x - 2$
(2) $x^2 - 3x - 2$
(3) $x^2 + 3x - 2$
(4) $x^2 + x + 2$
(5) $x^2 + x - 2$

13. The following quadratic equation has only one solution. What is it?

$$x^2 - 12x + 36 = 0$$

(1) 12
(2) 9
(3) 6
(4) 4
(5) 3

Answers and explanations start on page 86.

Types of Angles

When lines intersect, they form angles. The point where the lines intersect is called the vertex. The parts of the lines that extend from the vertex are called rays. The measure of an angle is the measure of the space between the rays. We measure angles in degrees (°).

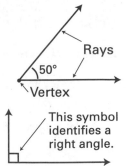

There are five types of angles you need to know. If you can recognize a right angle, the rest will be easy. A right angle is exactly 90°. The corner of a piece of paper is a right angle.

The remaining kinds of angles are also classified by their measures.

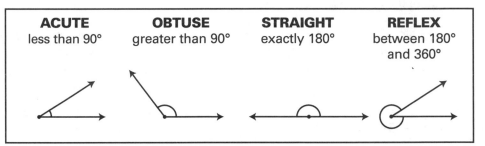

ACUTE	OBTUSE	STRAIGHT	REFLEX
less than 90°	greater than 90°	exactly 180°	between 180° and 360°

Complementary Angles

One way to explain angle relationships is to talk about their measures. When the sum of two angles is 90°, the angles are complementary angles. In the example below, the angles are numbered. $\angle 1$ means "angle 1" and $m\angle 1$ means "the measure of angle 1." Angles can also be identified by letters with the vertex in the center, as in the second example below.

$\angle 1$ and $\angle 2$ are complementary angles. If $m\angle 1$ is 40°, what is $m\angle 2$?

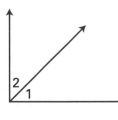

Since the angles are complementary, $m\angle 2 = 90° - 40°$, which equals **50°.**

Supplementary Angles

When the sum of two angles is 180°, the angles are supplementary angles. If you combine two angles that are supplementary, they form a straight angle.

$\angle AOB$ measures 105°. If $\angle AOC$ is a straight angle, what is the measure of $\angle BOC$?

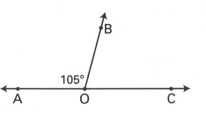

The angles are supplementary because they form a straight angle or a line. $180° - 105° = 75°$.

$m\angle BOC = $ **75°**

Measurement and Geometry Practice 1

A. Write the letter corresponding to the angle's name next to each angle.

a. right   **b. acute**   **c. obtuse**   **d. reflex**   **e. straight**

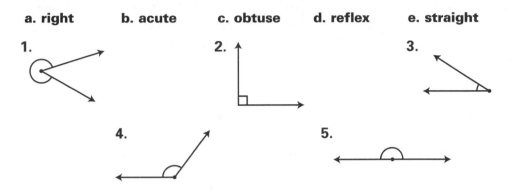

1.   **2.**   **3.**

4.   **5.**

B. For each angle measure, write the measure of its complementary and supplementary angles.

6. 32°   **7.** 76°   **8.** 15°

Complementary: _____   Complementary: _____   Complementary: _____

Supplementary: _____   Supplementary: _____   Supplementary: _____

C. Solve each problem. Then choose the correct answer.

<u>Questions 9–11</u> refer to the following figure.

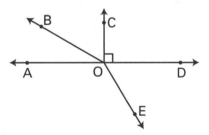

9. What kind of angle is ∠BOC?

    (1) right   **(4)** reflex
    (2) obtuse   **(5)** straight
    (3) acute

10. Which of these angles is adjacent to ∠COD? In other words, it shares a vertex AND a common side.

    (1) ∠AOB   **(4)** ∠BOE
    (2) ∠AOE   **(5)** ∠DOE
    (3) ∠AOD

11. If ∠AOD is a straight angle and ∠AOE measures 120°, what is the measure of ∠DOE?

    (1) 30°   **(4)** 120°
    (2) 60°   **(5)** 150°
    (3) 90°

12. Which of the following is true of angles 1 and 3 below?

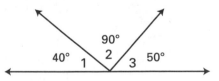

    (1) The angles are adjacent.
    (2) The angles are obtuse.
    (3) The angles are supplementary.
    (4) The angles are complementary.
    (5) The angles are straight angles.

Answers and explanations start on page 86.

Vertical Angles

When two lines intersect, they form four angles. The angles across from each other are called opposite angles, or vertical angles. The angles that are next to each other and share a common ray are adjacent angles.

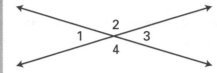

In the drawing, one pair of adjacent angles is ∠1 and ∠2. One pair of vertical angles is ∠1 and ∠3.

Vertical angles are always equal. When two lines intersect, you can know the measures of all the angles if you know one angle measure.

∠1 measures 60°. What are the measures of the remaining angles?

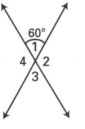

$m\angle 3 = 60°$ because it is vertical to ∠1.
$m\angle 2 = 120°$ because it is supplementary to ∠1.
$180° - 60° = 120°$
$m\angle 4 = 120°$ because it is vertical to ∠2.

From this example, you can see that it is important to have a reason for the decisions you make. On the GED Mathematics Test, don't guess the measure of an angle by how it looks. Look for clues in the problem and in the diagram that make it possible to *know* the measure of the angle.

Corresponding Angles

Parallel lines never cross. They are always an equal distance from each other. When a third line crosses a pair of parallel lines, it is called a transversal. A transversal creates vertical and corresponding angles. Corresponding angles are in the same position in relation to the transversal and the parallel lines. They always have the same measure as their corresponding angle.

Using your knowledge of angles, you can find the measure of every angle if the measure of one angle is known.

$p \parallel q$ means that lines p and q are parallel. If angle 3 measures 55°, what is the measure of angle 8?

∠3 and ∠7 are corresponding angles. They are both to the left of the transversal and below a parallel line. Therefore, $m\angle 7 = 55°$.

∠7 and ∠8 are supplementary angles. Subtract: $180° - 55° = 125°$.
$m\angle 8 = 125°$

There is more than one way to solve this problem. Remember to have a reason for every decision that you make.

Measurement and Geometry Practice 2

A. Fill in the measures of the angles as directed.

1. $m\angle 1 = 38°$

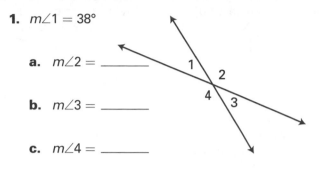

   a. $m\angle 2 =$ _____

   b. $m\angle 3 =$ _____

   c. $m\angle 4 =$ _____

2. $m\angle 2 = 57°$

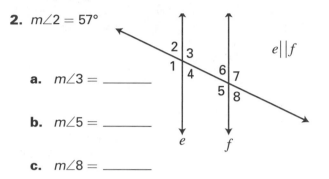

$e \| f$

   a. $m\angle 3 =$ _____

   b. $m\angle 5 =$ _____

   c. $m\angle 8 =$ _____

B. Solve each problem. Then choose the correct answer.

Questions 3 and 4 refer to the following figure.

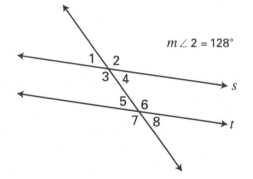

$m\angle 2 = 128°$

3. What must be true in order for $\angle 6$ to measure 128°?

   (1) $m\angle 1$ must equal 52°
   (2) $\angle 2$ and $\angle 6$ must be adjacent
   (3) $\angle 3$ and $\angle 2$ must be vertical angles
   (4) $m\angle 4$ must equal 52°
   (5) lines s and t must be parallel

4. If lines s and t are parallel, which of these pairs of angles have the same measure?

   (1) $\angle 1$ and $\angle 2$
   (2) $\angle 2$ and $\angle 4$
   (3) $\angle 4$ and $\angle 6$
   (4) $\angle 5$ and $\angle 8$
   (5) $\angle 6$ and $\angle 8$

Questions 5 and 6 refer to the following figure.

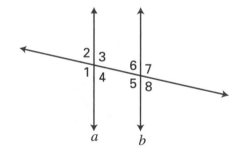

Lines a and b are parallel.

5. Which angle is adjacent to $\angle 5$?

   (1) $\angle 1$
   (2) $\angle 3$
   (3) $\angle 4$
   (4) $\angle 7$
   (5) $\angle 8$

6. Suppose $\angle 3$ measures 96°. Which angles also measure 96°?

   (1) $\angle 2$ and $\angle 4$
   (2) $\angle 4$ and $\angle 5$
   (3) $\angle 5$ and $\angle 7$
   (4) $\angle 6$ and $\angle 8$
   (5) $\angle 4$ and $\angle 8$

Answers and explanations start on page 86.

Properties of Figures

A triangle has three sides and three interior, or inside, angles. Triangles are categorized by the measures of their sides and angles. Study the following examples.

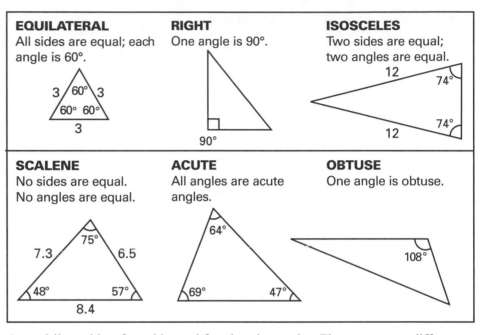

EQUILATERAL
All sides are equal; each angle is 60°.

3, 60°, 3, 60° 60°, 3

RIGHT
One angle is 90°.

90°

ISOSCELES
Two sides are equal; two angles are equal.

12, 74°, 74°, 12

SCALENE
No sides are equal. No angles are equal.

75°, 7.3, 6.5, 48°, 57°, 8.4

ACUTE
All angles are acute angles.

64°, 69°, 47°

OBTUSE
One angle is obtuse.

108°

A quadrilateral has four sides and four interior angles. There are many different kinds of quadrilaterals. Study these examples to see how quadrilaterals are categorized by the measures of their angles and sides.

SQUARE
All sides equal; 90° angles

RECTANGLE
Opposite sides equal; 90° angles

PARALLEL-OGRAM
Opposite sides equal; opposite angles equal

RHOMBUS
All sides equal; opposite angles equal

TRAPEZOID
Only one pair of sides is parallel

Solve Problems

The sum of the angles of a triangle equals 180°. The sum of the angles of any quadrilateral is 360°. You can use these facts to solve problems.

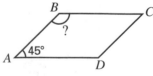

In parallelogram *ABCD*, ∠A measures 45°. What is the measure of ∠B?

In a parallelogram, the opposite angles have equal measures, so *m*∠C = 45°. Angles *B* and *D* also have equal measures.

Set up an equation using the facts that you know. Let *x* equal the measure of either ∠B or ∠D. The measure of ∠B is 135°.

$$45° + 45° + x + x = 360°$$
$$2x + 90° = 360°$$
$$2x = 270°$$
$$x = 135°$$

Measurement and Geometry Practice 3

A. Write the names of the types of triangles and quadrilaterals shown below.

1. _____   **2.** _____   **3.** _____   **4.** _____

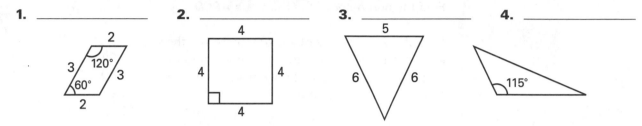

B. Write the names of the types of triangles and quadrilaterals described.

5. A four-sided figure has opposite sides of equal length. Two opposite angles measure 130° and two opposite angles measure 50°.

_____

6. A three-sided figure has three angles, each measuring 60°.

_____

7. A four-sided figure has four angles that measure 90°. Two of the sides measure 4 inches and the other two sides measure 8 inches.

_____

8. A three-sided figure has two acute angles and one angle that measures exactly 90°.

_____

C. Solve each problem. Then choose the correct answer.

9. Two of the angles in a triangle measure 30° and 60°. What kind of triangle is it?

(1) acute
(2) obtuse
(3) right
(4) equilateral
(5) isosceles

10. The measures of the angles for figure *ABCD* are given in the drawing below. What is the figure?

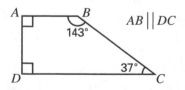

AB || *DC*

(1) square
(2) rectangle
(3) parallelogram
(4) rhombus
(5) trapezoid

11. A figure has four sides, each with the same length. What do you need to know to determine whether the figure is a square?

(1) the length of each side
(2) whether the opposite sides are parallel
(3) the measure of the angles
(4) the number of corners
(5) the number of angles

12. Figure *EFGH* is a rhombus. If ∠*FEH* measures 35°, what is the measure of ∠*EHG*?

(1) 35°
(2) 70°
(3) 145°
(4) 290°
(5) 360°

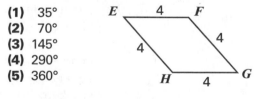

Answers and explanations start on page 86.

Find the Perimeter of Figures

Perimeter is the distance around the outside of a figure. There are formulas for finding the perimeter of special figures, but in general, add the lengths of all the sides of the figure to find the perimeter.

Find the perimeter of the rhombus *ABCD*.

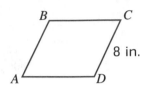

One of the properties of a rhombus is that the four sides are the same length. Since you know the measure of one side, multiply by 4, the number of sides, to find the perimeter.

8 × 4 = **32 inches**

Find the perimeter of the obtuse triangle *EFG*.

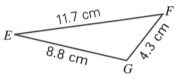

To find the perimeter of any triangle, add the three sides.

11.7 + 8.8 + 4.3 = **24.8 centimeters**

Solve for a Missing Side

In some cases, if you know the perimeter of a figure, you can use the properties of the figure to calculate the unknown length of a side.

The perimeter of rectangle *JKLM* is 40 feet. If the length of the rectangle is 13 feet, what is the width of the rectangle?

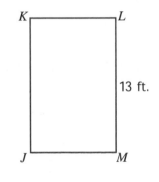

Since the figure is a rectangle, you know that both widths have the same measure.
Let *w* = the missing width.

$$13 + 13 + w + w = 40$$
$$26 + 2w = 40$$
$$2w = 14$$
$$w = \textbf{7 feet}$$

The properties of a figure may be very important to solving a problem.

A cement block is poured in the shape of the isosceles triangle shown at the right. The base is 6 feet wide. What is the perimeter of the cement block?

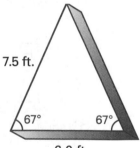

In an isosceles triangle, the sides that are opposite equal angles are also equal in length. Therefore, you know that the unknown side measures 7.5 feet.

Add: 7.5 + 7.5 + 6.0 = **21 feet**

The perimeter of the cement block is **21 feet**.

Measurement and Geometry Practice 4

A. Find the perimeter of each figure.

1.

3 cm | 3 cm
8 cm

3.

60°
5 in.
60°

5.

2.5 cm
2.5 cm
1.7 cm

2.

28.8 in.
16 in.
24 in.

4.

20 mm
16 mm
19 mm
37 mm

6.

$1\frac{1}{3}$ in.
$2\frac{2}{3}$ in.

B. Solve each problem. Then choose the correct answer.

7. A triangle has three angles that each measure 60°. One side of the triangle measures 15 centimeters. Which of the following expressions could be used to find the perimeter of the triangle?

(1) 60 × 3
(2) 15 × 3
(3) 60 + 60 + 15
(4) 15 + 15 + 60
(5) 15 × 60

8. A garden has the shape shown below.

6 ft.
4.5 ft. | 4.5 ft.
4.5 ft. | 4.5 ft.
6 ft.

A gardener wants to put a small fence around the garden to define the space. How many feet of fencing will she need?

(1) 15   **(4)** 36
(2) 18   **(5)** 90
(3) 30

9. The picture frame below is 2 inches wide. If the dimensions of the picture are 20 inches by 24 inches, what is the outside perimeter of the frame in inches?

(1) 44
(2) 48
(3) 88
(4) 96
(5) 104

10. One of the sides of a rhombus measures 6.8 centimeters. What is the perimeter, in centimeters, of the rhombus?

(1) 13.6
(2) 20.4
(3) 27.2
(4) 46.24
(5) Not enough information is given.

Answers and explanations start on page 87.

Understand the Meaning of Area

Area is the measure of space inside a figure. Area is measured using square units: square inches, square feet, and so on. When you measure area, you are saying how many of the square units are needed to cover the space.

How many tiles, measuring 1 foot on each side, will it take to cover this kitchen floor?

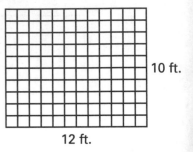

10 ft.

12 ft.

The floor is in the shape of a rectangle that is 12 feet long and 10 feet wide. If you divide the space into rows and columns, you can see you will need 12 × 10 = **120 tiles.** The area of the space is **120 square feet.**

Use Formulas to Find Area

When square units don't exactly fit inside a figure, you need a formula to find out how many will fit. Some of the area formulas from the GED Formulas page (also see page 60) are shown below.

square   Area = side^2

rectangle   Area = length × width

parallelogram   Area = base × height

triangle   Area = $\frac{1}{2}$ × base × height

What is the area, in square inches, of the triangle shown at the right?

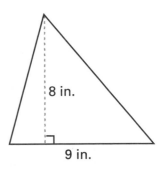

8 in.

9 in.

The base, or bottom, of the triangle is 9 inches. The height, which forms a right angle with the base, is 8 inches.

Use the formula: Area = $\frac{1}{2}$ × b × h

$\qquad\qquad\qquad = \frac{1}{2}$ × 9 × 8

$\qquad\qquad\qquad = \frac{1}{2}$ × 72 = 36 sq. in.

Area Problems

Using the formulas and your algebra skills, you can solve for a missing measure if all the other measures are known.

The area of a rectangular room is 180 square feet. If the room is 15 feet long, how wide is it?

What do you know?
The area is 180 square feet. The length is 15 feet. The width is missing.

Use the formula: Area = length × width

$\qquad\qquad\qquad 180 = 15w$

$\qquad\qquad\qquad \dfrac{180}{15} = \dfrac{15w}{15}$

$\qquad\qquad\qquad 12 = w$

The width of the room is **12 feet.**

A. Use the formulas on page 42 to find the area of each figure.

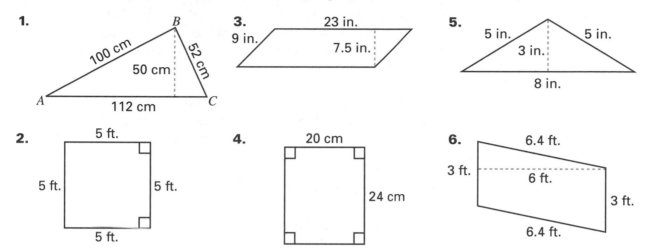

1.

B
100 cm
50 cm
52 cm
A
112 cm
C

3.
23 in.
9 in.
7.5 in.

5.
5 in.   5 in.
3 in.
8 in.

2.
5 ft.
5 ft.   5 ft.
5 ft.

4.
20 cm
24 cm

6.
6.4 ft.
3 ft.   6 ft.
3 ft.
6.4 ft.

C. Solve each problem. Then choose the correct answer.

7. A diagonal line is drawn through a rectangle as shown below. What is the area, in square centimeters, of the section marked *A*?

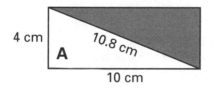

4 cm   10.8 cm
A
10 cm

(1) 20
(2) 24.8
(3) 28
(4) 40
(5) 43.2

8. A square has an area of 64 square inches. Which of the following expressions could be used to find the length, in inches, of 1 side?

(1) $\frac{64}{4}$

(2) 64^2

(3) $64 + 64 + 64 + 64$

(4) $\sqrt{8}$

(5) $\sqrt{64}$

9. The area of the rectangle below is 126 square inches.

9 in.

What is the length, in inches, of the rectangle?

(1) 7
(2) 14
(3) 31.5
(4) 54
(5) Not enough information is given.

10. The school flag is in the shape of an isosceles triangle. The base is 18 inches long and the height is 36 inches. The measures of the remaining sides are not given. What is the area, in square inches, of the flag?

(1) 648
(2) 324
(3) 216
(4) 90
(5) Not enough information is given.

Answers and explanations start on page 87.

Understand the Meaning of Volume

Volume is the measure of the space inside a three-dimensional object. Imagine you are comparing two closets to see which is bigger. Your main concern is probably how much each closet will hold.

Volume is measured in cubic units. For example, a cubic foot is a box shape that is 1 foot long, 1 foot wide, and 1 foot high. If a closet has a volume of 192 cubic feet, it means that the closet can hold exactly 192 boxes, each measuring 1 cubic foot.

Find Volume

Many three-dimensional objects are prisms. The bases (top and bottom faces) of a prism have the same shape. The sides are rectangles that join the bases. To find the volume of any prism, find the area of one of the bases and multiply by the height.

Volume = Area of Base × Height

The large moving box shown at the right is 3 feet long and 2.5 feet wide. What is the volume of the box?

The area of the base is
$3 \times 2.5 = 7.5$ square feet.

Multiply the area of the base by the height of 4 feet.
$7.5 \times 4 = $ **30 cubic feet**

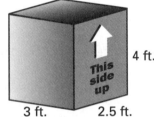

Solve Problems About Volume

Remember, volume only equals the area of the base multiplied by the height when the two bases are equal in size. When you take the GED Mathematics Test, you will be given a page of formulas (see page 60) to help you find the volume of other kinds of containers.

Sometimes you won't have a drawing to look at when you solve a geometry problem. As you read, try making a simple sketch so that you can visualize the problem.

A candy container has congruent, or equal, trapezoids on its ends. The area of each trapezoid is 3.5 square inches. If the container is 6 inches long, what is its volume?

Imagine the shape of the candy container. It probably looks something like this.

It isn't necessary to know how to find the area of the trapezoid because it is given in the problem. In this problem, the height of the prism is really its length because the container is turned so that the equal bases are on the ends instead of the top and bottom.

Multiply the area by the length. $3.5 \times 6 = $ **21 cubic inches**

Measurement and Geometry Practice 6

A. Find the volume of each figure.

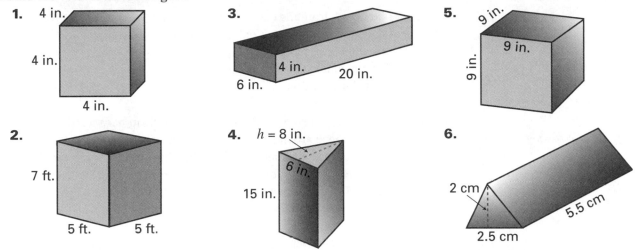

1. 4 in. 4 in. 4 in.

2. 7 ft. 5 ft. 5 ft.

3. 4 in. 6 in. 20 in.

4. $h = 8$ in. 6 in. 15 in.

5. 9 in. 9 in. 9 in.

6. 2 cm 2.5 cm 5.5 cm

B. Solve each problem. Then choose the correct answer.

7. The top of a cereal box is a rectangle with sides 3 inches wide and 7.5 inches long. Using the drawing below, what is the volume of the box in cubic inches?

(1)   4.4
(2)   21.5
(3)   115.5
(4)   247.5
(5)   264.0

7.5 in. 3 in.

Crunchy Crumbs

11 in.

8. A container has triangular ends. The base of each triangle is 8 inches and the height is 5 inches. Which expression can be used to find the volume, in cubic inches, of the container if the height of the box is 9 inches?

(1) $\frac{1}{2} \times 5 \times 8$
(2) $\frac{1}{2} \times 5 \times 8 + 9$
(3) $2(\frac{1}{2}) \times 5 \times 8$
(4) $\frac{1}{2} \times 5 \times 8 \times 9$
(5) $2(\frac{1}{2}) \times 5 \times 8 \times 9$

9. How many more cubic feet will the first box hold than the second?

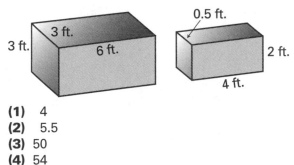

3 ft. 3 ft. 6 ft.

0.5 ft. 2 ft. 4 ft.

(1)   4
(2)   5.5
(3)   50
(4)   54
(5)   58

10. A building block has the same shape at each end. The volume of the block is 128 cubic inches. If the area of each end is 16 square inches, how many inches tall is the block?

(1)   4
(2)   8
(3)   96
(4)   112
(5) 2,048

Answers and explanations start on page 87.

Properties of Circles

A circle is a series of points that are each an equal distance from a center point. The series of points form a curved figure that we call a circle.

A straight line drawn from the center to any point on the edge of the circle is called the radius. A line that divides the circle in half, passing through its center point, is called the diameter. The diameter of a circle is always twice the length of its radius.

Many years ago, people discovered a special relationship between the diameter of a circle and the distance around its circumference, or outside edge. For any circle, the circumference is about 3.14 times the diameter. This relationship is called pi, represented by the symbol π. Pi represents a number with an infinite number of decimal digits. When you take the GED Mathematics Test, use the decimal 3.14 for π. (For a quick estimate, use the number 3 for π.)

Pi allows us to find the circumference and area of a circle and the volume of a cylinder, a three-dimensional figure with circles as the bases. Use these formulas.

Circumference = $\pi \times$ diameter
Area = $\pi \times$ radius^2
Volume of a cylinder = $\pi \times$ radius$^2 \times$ height

Find the Circumference

Study how the formulas are applied in these examples.

Find the circumference and area of circle *O*.
Circumference = $\pi \times$ diameter
$\qquad$ = 3.14 $\times$ 6
$\qquad$ = **18.84 inches**

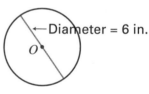

Remember, the radius is half the diameter, so the radius of circle *O* is 6 $\div$ 2 = 3 inches.

Area = $\pi \times$ radius^2
$\qquad$ = 3.14 $\times$ 3^2
$\qquad$ = 3.14 $\times$ 9
$\qquad$ = **28.26 square inches**

Find the Area

Notice how the first part of the volume formula is actually the area formula for a circle. All you are doing in the volume formula is multiplying the area of one of the bases by the height.

Find the volume of the cylinder.
Volume = $\pi \times$ radius$^2 \times$ height
$\qquad$ = 3.14 $\times$ 2$^2 \times$ 6
$\qquad$ = 3.14 $\times$ 4 $\times$ 6
$\qquad$ = **75.36 cubic feet**

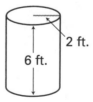

Measurement and Geometry Practice 7

A. Find the circumference and area of each circle. Use 3.14 for π.

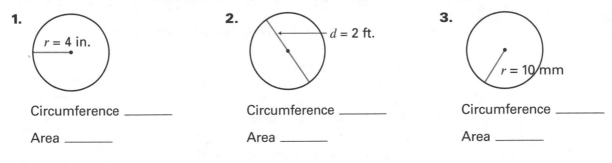

1.

r = 4 in.

Circumference _____

Area _____

2.

d = 2 ft.

Circumference _____

Area _____

3.

r = 10 mm

Circumference _____

Area _____

B. Find the volume of each cylinder. Use 3.14 for π. Round to the nearest hundredth.

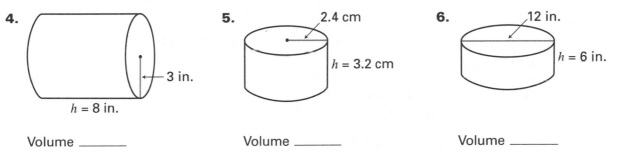

4.

3 in.

h = 8 in.

Volume _____

5.

2.4 cm

h = 3.2 cm

Volume _____

6.

12 in.

h = 6 in.

Volume _____

C. Solve each problem. Then choose the correct answer.

7. Sean has a circular hot tub with a radius of 4 feet. He wants to put no-slip tile around the edge of the tub. What is the distance, in feet, around the outside edge of the tub?

(1) 12.56
(2) 25.12
(3) 50.24
(4) 200.96
(5) Not enough information is given.

8. The Youngs are building a brick border around a small tree in their backyard. The diagram below shows the space set aside for the tree. What is the area of the brick border to the nearest square foot?

(1) 79
(2) 66
(3) 28
(4) 16
(5) 13

BORDER
2 ft.
TREE
3 ft.

Questions 9 and 10 refer to the drawing.

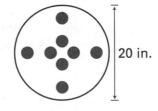

20 in.

9. What is the circumference, in inches, of the large metal disk?

(1) 31.4   **(4)** 628
(2) 62.8   **(5)** 1,256
(3) 314

10. Each of the 8 holes cut in the disk has a 1-inch diameter. What is the area in square inches of the remaining metal on the metal disk?

(1) 0.785   **(4)** 307.72
(2) 6.28   **(5)** 314
(3) 62.8

Answers and explanations start on page 87.

Solve Problems About Perimeter

A regular figure has properties that make it easy for us to recognize its name and shape. An irregular figure can have any shape. Find the perimeter of an irregular figure by finding the total of all the sides. If the measure of a side isn't given, look for a way to find the length using the known sides.

What is the perimeter of the figure shown at the right?

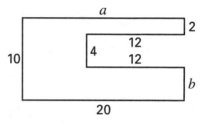

1. Find any missing measures.
    ● The top edge (*a*) must have the same measure as the bottom edge: 20.
    ● The bottom right edge (*b*) is unlabeled, but the total of all the right edges must equal 10, the measure of the left edge.
      $2 + 4 + b = 10$, so $b = 4$
2. Add all the side lengths:
    $10 + 20 + 4 + 12 + 4 + 12 + 2 + 20 = \textbf{84}$

Solve Problems About Area

Irregular figures are usually made up of regular figures. To find the total area, divide the irregular figure into regular figures, and find the area of each regular figure. Then add to find the total area of the irregular figure.

What is the area of the living room shown here?

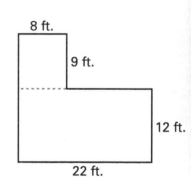

1. Separate the L-shaped room into two rectangles.
2. Find the area of each rectangle.
    Top rectangle: $9 \times 8 = 72$ sq. ft.
    Bottom rectangle: $22 \times 12 = 264$ sq. ft.
3. Add to find the area of the room.
    $72 + 264 = \textbf{336 square feet}$

Sometimes there will be more than one way to divide an irregular shape. Choose the way that results in the fewest number of regular figures whenever you can. Think ahead to make sure you will have all the measures you need to find the area of the individual figures you created.

A Koi fishpond at a children's hospital has an unusual shape. Find the area of the fishpond.

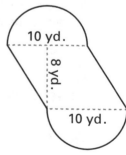

1. The fishpond is a parallelogram with two half circles attached.
2. Since two halves make a whole, find the area of one whole circle.
    If the diameter is 10, the radius is 5.
    Area: $3.14 \times 5^2 = 78.5$ sq. yd.
3. Find the area of the parallelogram.
    Area: $8 \times 10 = 80$ sq. yd.
4. Add: $78.5 + 80 = \textbf{158.5 square yards}$

Measurement and Geometry Practice 8

A. Find the perimeter of each figure.

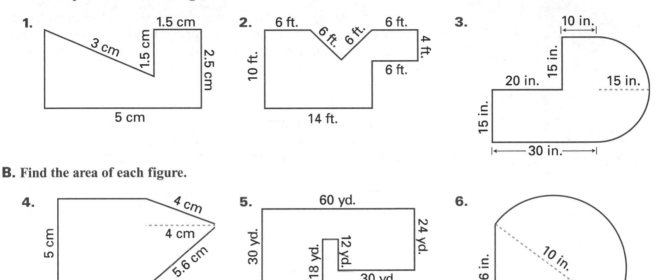

1.

1.5 cm
3 cm
1.5 cm
2.5 cm
5 cm

2.

6 ft.
6 ft.
6 ft.
6 ft.
10 ft.
4 ft.
6 ft.
14 ft.

3.

10 in.
15 in.
20 in.
15 in.
15 in.
30 in.

B. Find the area of each figure.

4.

4 cm
4 cm
5.6 cm
5 cm
5 cm

5.

60 yd.
30 yd.
18 yd.
12 yd.
24 yd.
30 yd.
24 yd.

6.

10 in.
6 in.
8 in.

C. Solve each problem. Then choose the correct answer.

Question 7 refers to the following figure.

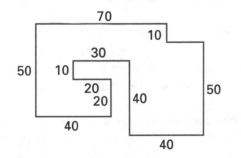

70
10
30
50
10
20
20
40
50
40
40

7. The diagram above shows the top floor of a museum. All lengths are in feet. What is the perimeter, in feet, of the floor?

- **(1)** 280
- **(2)** 290
- **(3)** 370
- **(4)** 400
- **(5)** Not enough information is given.

Question 8 refers to the following figure.

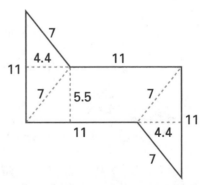

7
4.4
11
11
7
5.5
7
11
11
4.4
7

8. In the figure, all lengths are in yards. What is the area, in square yards, of the figure?

- **(1)** 24.2
- **(2)** 48.4
- **(3)** 84.7
- **(4)** 108.9
- **(5)** 532.4

Answers and explanations start on page 87.

Rules of Congruence

Two figures are congruent when they are exactly the same shape and size. In other words, if you put one figure on top of the other, they would match perfectly. Every point, side, and angle would be identical.

Early mathematicians figured out that you could tell whether two figures were congruent just by looking or by comparing measurements, but they wanted more. They wanted a way to prove that two figures were congruent. Soon they had developed these rules for triangles.

Two triangles are congruent if
- The three sides are congruent. (SSS)
- Two sides and the angle between them are congruent. (SAS)
- Two angles and the side between them are congruent. (ASA)

In the drawings below, the small marks in the sides and angles of the figures mean congruence. You know that $\angle A$ and $\angle X$ are congruent because they have the same number of marks.

Are triangles *XYZ* and *ABC* congruent?

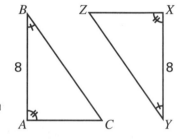

1. Look for angles and sides with equal measures: $m\angle B = m\angle Y$, $\overline{AB} = \overline{XY}$, and $m\angle A = m\angle X$.
2. Do you have enough information to draw a conclusion? You know that two corresponding angles are equal and the sides between them are equal.
3. **The triangles are congruent because of the rule ASA.**

Did you notice that in this example, the figures are congruent, but one is turned? This makes it harder to find the corresponding parts. You will often have to turn or flip the figure in your mind so that both are turned the same way. If this is difficult, you can redraw one of the figures so that they are turned the same way.

Find a Missing Measure

Sometimes you may have to solve for a measure to prove two figures are congruent. In the problem below, the symbol $\cong$ means "is congruent to."

$\triangle DEF \cong \triangle TUV$. What is the measure of $\angle D$?

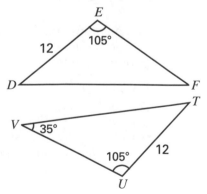

What angle in $\triangle TUV$ corresponds to $\angle D$?
$\angle T \cong \angle D$
You know two of the angles in $\triangle TUV$.
Solve for the missing angle.
$$35° + 105° + \angle T = 180°$$
$$140° + \angle T = 180°$$
$$\angle T = 40°$$

Since $\angle T \cong \angle D$, **$m\angle D = 40°$.**

A. Decide whether or not each pair of figures is congruent. Write the reason for your decision.

1.

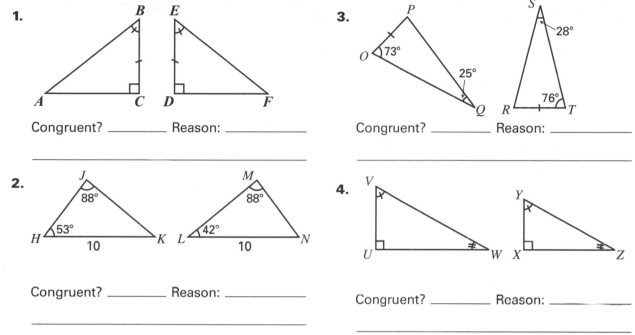

Congruent? _____ Reason: _____

_____

2.

Congruent? _____ Reason: _____

_____

3.

Congruent? _____ Reason: _____

_____

4.

Congruent? _____ Reason: _____

_____

B. Solve each problem. Then choose the correct answer.

5. Triangles *ABC* and *EFG* are isosceles. Both triangles have the angle measures 90°, 45°, and 45°. Both have a base that measures 8 inches. Which is a true statement about triangles *ABC* and *EFG*?

(1) The triangles are congruent because of the AAA rule.
(2) The only corresponding sides are opposite 90° angles.
(3) The triangles are congruent because of the ASA rule.
(4) There is not enough information to be sure that the triangles are congruent.
(5) These triangles could not be congruent.

6. △*HJK* ≅ △*MLN*. Side *JK* ≅ Side ?

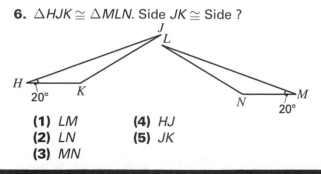

(1) *LM*   **(4)** *HJ*
(2) *LN*   **(5)** *JK*
(3) *MN*

7. Using only the information from the diagram, which rule can be used to prove these triangles are congruent?

(1) SAS
(2) SSS
(3) ASA
(4) AAA
(5) Not enough information is given.

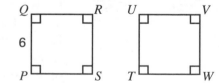

8. Other figures can also be congruent. Which item of information would help you know whether or not these squares are congruent?

(1) the length of side *QR*
(2) the length of side *PS*
(3) the measure of ∠*UTW*
(4) the measure of ∠*UVW*
(5) the length of side *TU*

Answers and explanations start on page 88.

Decide Whether or Not Two Figures Are Similar

Similar figures have the same shape, but they have a different size. Even though the sides are different lengths, the ratios of the lengths of their corresponding sides are the same.

Are these rectangles similar?

Find the ratio of the lengths of the two rectangles.

$$\frac{\text{length of } ABCD}{\text{length of } EFGH} = \frac{8}{4} = \frac{2}{1}$$

Now find the ratio of the widths.

$$\frac{\text{width of } ABCD}{\text{width of } EFGH} = \frac{6}{3} = \frac{2}{1}$$

Since the proportions are equal, the figures are similar. The symbol for similar is $\sim$, so for the example above, you can write **ABCD $\sim$ EFGH**.

If two triangles have the same angle measures, they are similar triangles. If you don't know the angle measures, two figures are similar if the lengths of corresponding sides have the same proportion.

Are triangles *JKL* and *JMN* similar?

Side *JM* is 3 times side *JK*.
Side *NM* is 3 times side *KL*.
Side *JN* is 3 times side *JL*.

The ratio of the sides in $\triangle JKL$ is in proportion to the sides in $\triangle JMN$ because the corresponding sides all have a ratio of 3 to 1.

Solve Practical Problems

Similar right triangles are often used as a way to measure things that would be very difficult to measure directly.

What is the distance across the river shown in the diagram?

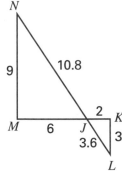

A surveyor stakes out two right triangles as shown. Since all corresponding angles are equal, the triangles are similar. The 15-foot length corresponds to the 50-foot length. The 12-foot length corresponds to length *x*. Set up a proportion and solve.

$$\frac{15}{50} = \frac{12}{x}$$
$$50(12) = 15x$$
$$600 = 15x$$
$$40 = x$$

The distance across the river is **40 feet.**

Measurement and Geometry Practice 10

A. Decide whether or not each pair of figures is similar. Write the reason for your decision.

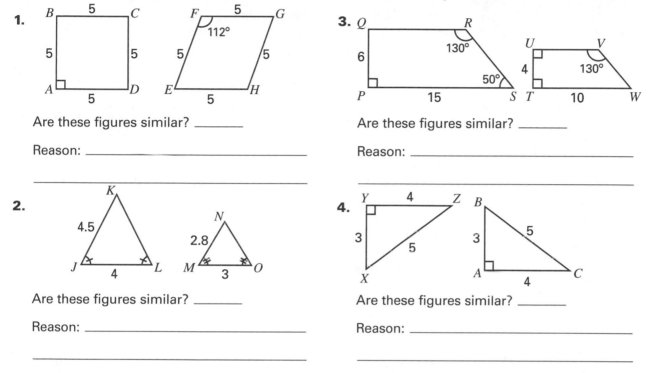

1.

Are these figures similar? _____

Reason: _____

_____

3. Q

Are these figures similar? _____

Reason: _____

_____

2.

Are these figures similar? _____

Reason: _____

_____

4.

Are these figures similar? _____

Reason: _____

_____

B. Solve each problem. Then choose the correct answer.

<u>Questions 5 and 6</u> refer to the following drawing.

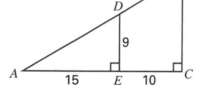

5. The ramp above connects two vertical supports, forming two similar triangles: $\triangle ADE \sim \triangle ABC$. Side AC corresponds to which side in the other triangle?

(1) side AE
(2) side DE
(3) side BC
(4) side AD
(5) side AB

6. What is the length of side BC?

(1) 3.6   **(4)** 18
(2) 6   **(5)** 20
(3) 15

7. In the late afternoon, a tree casts a 30-foot long shadow. At the same time, a traffic sign that is 6 feet in height casts a 4.5-foot shadow. How many feet tall is the tree?

(1) 27
(2) 40
(3) 46
(4) 135
(5) 180

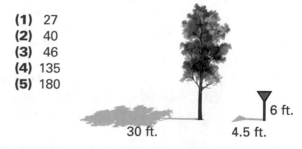

8. Circle O has a radius of 4 inches. Circle P has a diameter of 8 inches. Which of the following is a true statement?

(1) Circle O is bigger than circle P.
(2) Circle P is bigger than circle O.
(3) Circle O has more area than circle P.
(4) Circles O and P are similar.
(5) Circles O and P are congruent.

Answers and explanations start on page 88.

The Pythagorean Relationship

The Pythagorean Relationship was named by the ancient Greeks, although there is evidence that many other ancient civilizations had discovered the special relationship between the legs of a right triangle and its hypotenuse (longest side).

Put in words, the Pythagorean Relationship states that the sum of the squares of the legs of a right triangle equals the square of the hypotenuse.

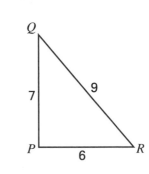

We can also write the relationship as a formula: $c^2 = a^2 + b^2$, where a and b are the legs of the right triangle, and c is the hypotenuse.

You can use the Pythagorean Relationship to decide whether or not a triangle is a right triangle when the angle measures are not given.

Is triangle *PQR* a right triangle?

Substitute the values into the formula.

$$c^2 = a^2 + b^2$$
$$9^2 = 6^2 + 7^2$$
$$81 = 36 + 49$$
$$81 \neq 85$$

△*PQR* is not a right triangle.

Solve Application Problems

Many real-life problems can be solved using the Pythagorean Relationship.

A contractor uses a diagonal brace to make sure a wall doesn't shift during construction. The brace is 20 feet long. If the brace is placed on the ground 12 feet from the wall, how high up on the wall will it reach?

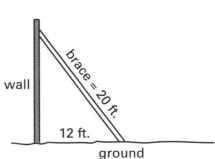

The wall and the ground form a right angle. The diagonal brace is the hypotenuse of the right triangle. Substitute the values and solve.

$$c^2 = a^2 + b^2 \qquad \text{Substitute the values into the formula.}$$
$$20^2 = 12^2 + b^2 \qquad \text{Square the known values.}$$
$$400 = 144 + b^2 \qquad \text{Simplify by subtracting 144 from each side.}$$
$$256 = b^2$$
$$\sqrt{256} = \sqrt{b^2} \qquad \text{Find the square root of each side.}$$
$$16 = b \qquad \text{The brace will reach up to } \textbf{16 feet} \text{ on the wall.}$$

Measurement and Geometry Practice 11

A. Each problem shows the measures of three sides of a triangle. Decide whether or not the triangle is a right triangle. Check *Yes* or *No*.

1. $a = 5$
$b = 12$
$c = 13$
Yes ___ No ___

3. $a = 3$
$b = 4$
$c = 5$
Yes ___ No ___

5. $a = 5$
$b = 6$
$c = 8$
Yes ___ No ___

7. $a = 1.5$
$b = 2$
$c = 2.5$
Yes ___ No ___

2. $a = 2$
$b = 2$
$c = 3$
Yes ___ No ___

4. $a = 15$
$b = 36$
$c = 39$
Yes ___ No ___

6. $a = 4$
$b = 8$
$c = 9$
Yes ___ No ___

8. $a = 9$
$b = 20$
$c = 21$
Yes ___ No ___

B. Solve each problem. Then choose the correct answer.

9. Lake City is 50 miles due north of Midtown. Bountiful is 40 miles due east of Midtown. Which of the following represents the distance, in miles, from Lake City to Bountiful?

(1) $\sqrt{1,000}$
(2) $\sqrt{2,000}$
(3) $\sqrt{4,000}$
(4) $\sqrt{4,100}$
(5) $\sqrt{8,100}$

10. A ladder is leaning on the side of a house as shown. How far, in feet, is the ladder from the bottom of the house?

(1) 5
(2) 7
(3) 9
(4) 11
(5) 13

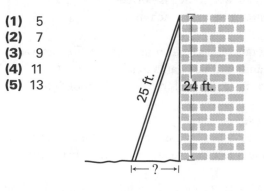

11. The rectangle below is divided in half by a diagonal line.

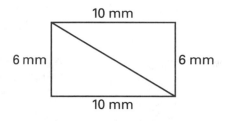

Which of the following equations could be used to find the length of the diagonal?

(1) $6 + 10 = c^2$
(2) $(6 + 10)^2 = c^2$
(3) $6^2 + 10^2 = c^2$
(4) $10^2 - 6^2 = c^2$
(5) $10^2 - a^2 = b^2$

12. The hypotenuse of a right triangle is 13.5 centimeters. Which of the following must be true?

(1) One leg is longer than 13.5 centimeters.
(2) Both legs are longer than 13.5 centimeters.
(3) The hypotenuse must be at least twice as long as the shortest leg.
(4) The hypotenuse equals the sum of the legs.
(5) The hypotenuse is longer than either leg.

Answers and explanations start on page 88.

THE FIVE-STEP STRATEGY

To solve word problems, you need to have a strategy for how to approach and solve the problem. You can use the five-step strategy below to help you make sense of any word problem.

STEP 1. Read and understand the problem.
STEP 2. Find the necessary facts and information.
STEP 3. Choose the correct operations.
STEP 4. Solve the problem.
STEP 5. Check your answer to make sure it makes sense.

Sample Question

Max plans to save $125 a month. His goal is to save $2,400 to buy a used car. If Max saves $125 each month for 12 months, how much more does he need to save to reach his goal?

(1) $125
(2) $900
(3) $1,500
(4) $2,400
(5) $3,900

Think It Through

Q: What is the question asking?
A: The question asks how much more money Max needs to save to reach his goal, the price of the car.

Q: What facts do you need to solve the problem?
A: You need the amount being saved each month ($125), the number of months (12), and the total amount to be saved ($2,400).

Q: In this multi-step problem, which operations should you use: addition, subtraction, multiplication, or division?
A: Since Max saves the same amount for 12 months, you should multiply. Then subtract the amount from the total he needs to save.

Q: Solve the problem. Which answer choice is correct?
A: Choice 1 ($125) is the amount he saves each month.
Choice 2 is correct.
Choice 3 ($1,500) is how much he saved so far, not the final answer.
Choice 4 ($2,400) is the amount Max wants to save.
Choice 5 incorrectly adds (instead of subtracts) the 12-month total.

Q: Does the answer make sense?
A: Yes, the answer makes sense. Since the amount Max already saved ($1,500) is more than half, the amount left to save should be less than half.

Answer and Explanation

(2) $900 To find the amount Max saved over 12 months, multiply $125 by 12: $125 \times 12 = \$1,500$. Subtract that amount from the cost of the car: $\$2,400 - \$1,500 = \$900$. That is less than half of $2,400.

Some word problems may have extra information. Other problems may not have all the facts you need to calculate the missing facts. For problems that don't have enough information, choose (5) Not enough information is given.

Sample Question

Tico's goal is to save $1,000 this year. So far, he has saved $120 each month for 6 months. If Tico meets his goal, how much more will he save this year compared to last year?

(1) $120
(2) $280
(3) $720
(4) $1,000
(5) Not enough information is given.

SAVINGS				
Deposit				$120	00
Deposit				$120	00
Deposit				$120	00
Deposit				$120	00
Deposit				$120	00
Deposit				$120	00

Think It Through

Q: What is the question asking?
A: The question asks how much more money Tico will save this year <u>compared to last year</u>.

Q: What facts or information do you need to solve the problem?
A: You need to know Tico's savings for this year ($1,000) and the amount he saved last year. The problem does not tell you how much he saved last year.

Answer and Explanation

(5) Not enough information is given. There is no way to figure out how much money Tico saved last year. Therefore, choice 5 is correct.

Guided Practice

Use the hints to help you solve the problems, and explain your answers.

HINT: Which operations should you use? In what order would you perform them?

1. Carpet Wholesale has 240 employees. The number of installers is 12 less than three times the number of salespeople. How many salespeople work for Carpet Wholesale?

   (1) 63   **(2)** 84   **(3)** 156   **(4)** 172   **(5)** 228

   Answer _____ is correct because _____

   _____

HINT: What facts do you need to solve the problem? Do you have all the facts that you need?

2. Grace earns $500 per month plus a 15% commission on her total sales. During November and December, she earned $2,670. What were her total sales in November?

   (1) $515   **(4)** $2,170
   (2) $575   **(5)** Not enough information is given.
   (3) $1,335

   Answer _____ is correct because _____

   _____

Answers and explanations start on page 88.

Choose the correct answer. Use the hints to help you solve the problems.

1. Ron's Sandwiches has started selling salads. Ron notices that customers order three times as many garden salads as chicken salads. On Tuesday, Ron sold a total of 24 garden and chicken salads. What number were chicken salads?

   THINK: What operations should you use to find the total number of salads if you know the number of chicken salads?

   (1) 4
   (2) 6
   (3) 8
   (4) 12
   (5) 18

2. One of the angles in an isosceles triangle measures 30°. What are the measures of the other two angles?

   THINK: What are the properties of an isosceles triangle? Do you have the information you need to find the measures of the other angles?

   (1) 30° and 120°
   (2) 30° and 150°
   (3) 60° and 60°
   (4) 75° and 75°
   (5) Not enough information is given.

3. Last year, Ellen earned $12.50 an hour. Recently, her boss gave her an 8% raise. How much more is she being paid per hour?

   THINK: The question asks how much more she makes per hour. Be sure to answer that question.

   (1) $0.08
   (2) $0.80
   (3) $1.00
   (4) $13.50
   (5) $20.50

4. In the figure below, transversal *a* crosses two parallel lines, *b* and *c*. If ∠1 measures 80°, what is the measure of ∠8?

   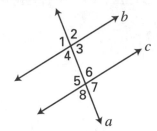

   THINK: What is the relationship between ∠1 and ∠8? How can you use other angles to help you find the correct relationship?

   (1) 10°
   (2) 80°
   (3) 100°
   (4) 120°
   (5) Not enough information is given.

5. Spencer's business pays him $0.28 per mile when he uses his car for work. During May, he went on two business trips. The first was twice as many miles as the second. If he was paid $126, how many miles long was the first trip?

   THINK: What operations would you use if you know the number of miles for each trip?

   (1) 450
   (2) 300
   (3) 252
   (4) 150
   (5) 126

6. In the figure below, ∠AFE is a straight angle. What angle is complementary to ∠AFB?

   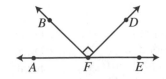

   THINK: Use information that is given in the figure but is not stated in the problem.

   (1) ∠AFE
   (2) ∠AFB
   (3) ∠BFD
   (4) ∠DFE
   (5) Not enough information is given.

Choose the one best answer to each question.

7. Janette pays $39 per month for a fitness center membership. She also pays $30 for each craft class she takes. If she takes four craft classes a year, how much does she pay to the fitness center per year?

(1) $120
(2) $468
(3) $588
(4) $828
(5) Not enough information is given.

8. Suppose you need to find the volume, in cubic feet, of the barrel below. What additional information do you need?

4 ft.

(1) the width of the barrel
(2) the circumference of the base
(3) the diameter of the base
(4) the distance around the barrel
(5) the height of the barrel

9. The length of a rectangular oil painting is 5 inches less than twice its width. If the perimeter of the painting is 62 inches, what is its width in inches?

(1) 12
(2) 15.5
(3) 19
(4) 31
(5) 57

10. David completed 50 pages of a reading assignment in 60 minutes. At the same rate, how many minutes will it take him to read 240 pages?

(1) 110
(2) 130
(3) 240
(4) 288
(5) Not enough information is given.

Questions 11 and 12 refer to the figure below.

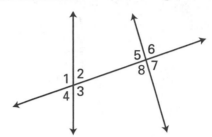

11. What do you know about ∠2 and ∠4?

(1) They are adjacent angles.
(2) They are supplementary.
(3) They are right angles.
(4) They are congruent.
(5) They are complementary.

12. If the measure of ∠1 is 110°, what is the measure of ∠8?

(1) 40°
(2) 70°
(3) 90°
(4) 110°
(5) Not enough information is given.

13. Carla is twice as old as Lamar. Jesse is 4 years older than Carla. If their combined age is 134 years, how old is Lamar?

(1) 26
(2) 34
(3) 65
(4) 71
(5) Not enough information is given.

14. At a new school, every classroom has 18 students or fewer. If there are 224 students at the school, what is the least number of classrooms that it has?

(1) 12
(2) 13
(3) 14
(4) 15
(5) Not enough information is given.

Answers and explanations start on page 89.

THE FORMULAS PAGE

Formulas show a process for solving certain kinds of problems. When you take the GED Mathematics Test, you will be given a page of formulas to use. You can look at this page if you need help during the test.

This page is reproduced for your use below.

GED Formulas Page

AREA of a:

square	Area = side^2
rectangle	Area = length × width
parallelogram	Area = base × height
triangle	Area = $\frac{1}{2}$ × base × height
trapezoid	Area = $\frac{1}{2}$ × (base$_1$ + base$_2$) × height
circle	Area = π × radius^2; π is approximately equal to 3.14

PERIMETER of a:

square	Perimeter = 4 × side
rectangle	Perimeter = 2 × length + 2 × width
triangle	Perimeter = side$_1$ + side$_2$ + side$_3$

CIRCUMFERENCE of a circle

Circumference = π × diameter; π is approximately equal to 3.14

VOLUME of a:

cube	Volume = edge^3
rectangular container	Volume = length × width × height
square pyramid	Volume = $\frac{1}{3}$ × (base edge)^2 × height
cylinder	Volume = π × radius^2 × height; π is approximately equal to 3.14
cone	Volume = $\frac{1}{3}$ × π × radius^2 × height; π is approximately equal to 3.14

COORDINATE GEOMETRY   distance between points = $\sqrt{(x_2 - x_1)^2 (y_2 - y_1)^2}$; (x_1, y_1) and (x_2, y_2) are two points in a plane.

slope of a line = $\frac{y_2 - y_1}{x_2 - x_1}$; (x_1, y_1) and (x_2, y_2) are two points on a line.

PYTHAGOREAN RELATIONSHIP

$a^2 + b^2 = c^2$; a and b are legs and c the hypotenuse of a right triangle.

MEASURES OF CENTRAL TENDENCY   mean = $\frac{x_1 + x_2 + ... + x_n}{n}$; where x's are the values for which a mean is desired, and n is the total number of values for x.

median = the middle value of an odd number of ordered scores, and halfway between the two middle values of an even number of ordered scores.

SIMPLE INTEREST   interest = principal × rate × time

DISTANCE   distance = rate × time

TOTAL COST   total cost = (number of units) × (price per unit)

Set-up problems are designed to see whether or not you know the correct process for solving a problem. The five answer choices for a set-up problem can be in the form of an expression, equation, or function. Some of these will be based on the formulas from the formulas page.

Sample Question

Which of the following expressions can be used to find the area of the figure shown below?

(1) $2(13) + 2(9)$
(2) $13(9)$
(3) $\frac{1}{2}(13)(6.7)$
(4) $13(6.7)$
(5) $13 + 6.7 + 9$

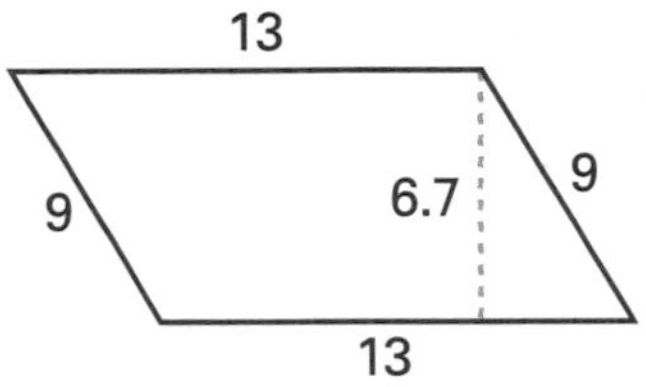

Think It Through

Q: What process are you being asked to show?
A: The problem asks you to show the process for finding the area of a parallelogram—the shape shown in the figure.

Q: Is there a formula for this process? If not, how would you put the process in words?
A: Under the Area section of the formulas page, the formula for finding the area of a parallelogram is given: Area = base × height. The figure gives the base as 13 and the height as 6.7.

Answer and Explanation

(4) 13(6.7) This is the only choice that multiplies the base by the height of this figure; therefore, choice 4 is correct. The other choices use formulas for other shapes or are perimeter formulas.

Guided Practice

Use the hints to help you solve the problems, and explain your answers.

HINT: Is there a formula you can use? How would you state the process in words?

1. Maggie bought 3 books at $5 each and 2 books at $4 each. Which expression could be used to find the total cost in dollars?

   (1) $3 + 5 + 2 + 4$ **(3)** $3(5) + 2(4)$ **(5)** $3(2) + 5(4)$
   (2) $3(4) + 5(2)$ **(4)** $3(4)(5)(2)$

   Answer _____ is correct because _____

   _____

HINT: If your equation isn't among the choices, is there another equation that means the same thing?

2. The side measure of a square is 7 inches. Each of the interior angles measure 90°. Which of the following equations could be used to solve for the area (A) of the square?

   (1) $A = 4(7)$ **(3)** $A = 7(90)$ **(5)** $A = 4(7 + 90)$
   (2) $A = 7^2$ **(4)** $A = 2(7) + 2(90)$

   Answer _____ is correct because _____

   _____

Answers and explanations start on page 89.

Choose the correct answer. Use the hints to help you solve the problems.

1. The courtyard of an apartment complex is in the shape of a rectangle. The area of the courtyard is 204 square meters. If the length is 12 meters, which equation can be used to solve for the width (*w*) in meters?

THINK: How can you rewrite the area formula so that you are solving for the width?

(1) $w = \frac{204}{12}$

(2) $w = \frac{12}{204}$

(3) $w = 12(204)$

(4) $w = \frac{204 - 2(12)}{2}$

(5) $w = 204 - 12$

2. On two math tests, Jasmine has 86 points and 88 points. She needs a mean score, or average, of 90 to get an A. Which expression can be used to find how many points (*p*) Jasmine would have to get on a third test to earn an A?

THINK: How can you put the process of finding an average in algebraic terms?

(1) $86 + 88 + p$

(2) $3(86 + 88 + p)$

(3) $\frac{86 + 88 + p}{3}$

(4) $\frac{86 + 88}{3p}$

(5) $\frac{p}{86 + 88}$

3. Which expression could be used to find the volume of the box below?

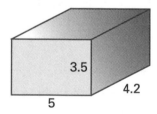

THINK: Which expression uses the formula for volume of a rectangle from the GED formulas page?

(1) 5(4.2)

(2) 2(5) + 2(4.2)

(3) 3.5(5 + 4.2)

(4) 5(4.2)(3.5)

(5) 5^3

4. Marcus borrowed $600 from his sister. He agreed to pay her back the whole amount plus 5% interest in 2 years. Which expression could be used to find the amount Marcus will pay his sister in 2 years?

THINK: Which expression revises the interest formula so that it shows the <u>total amount to be paid back</u>?

(1) $600(2)(0.05)

(2) $600(2)(0.05) + $600

(3) $600 − $600(2)(0.05)

(4) 2($600 + $600 × 0.05)

(5) $600 + $600(2)(5)

5. The perimeter of triangle *ABC* (shown below) is 21.2 centimeters. The area is 19.55 square centimeters. Which of the following expressions could be used to find the triangle's height?

THINK: Which expression uses the height of a triangle as a variable?

(1) 19.55 − 5.3 − 7.4

(2) $\frac{21.2}{2(8.5)}$

(3) $\frac{2(21.2)}{8.5}$

(4) $\frac{19.55}{2(8.5)}$

(5) $\frac{2(19.55)}{8.5}$

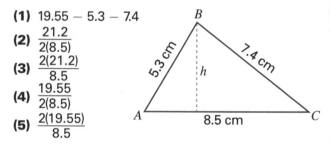

6. Brian plans to drive 1,430 miles to visit his family. He needs to finish the drive in 3 days or less. If he averages 65 miles per hour, which equation can be used to find how much time (*t*) the trip will take in hours?

THINK: What is the relationship between distance, rate, and time?

(1) $t = \frac{1,430}{65}$

(2) $t = \frac{1,430}{3}$

(3) $t = \frac{1,430(3)}{65}$

(4) $1,430 = 65(3)t$

(5) $65t = \frac{1,430}{3}$

Choose the one best answer to each question.

7. Mila drove 3 hours at an average rate of 70 miles per hour and 2 hours at an average rate of 55 miles per hour. Which expression could be used to find how many miles Mila drove during the trip?

(1) $(2 + 3)(70)(55)$
(2) $3(70) + 2(55)$
(3) $(70 \div 3) + (55 \div 2)$
(4) $2(70) + 3(55)$
(5) $2(3)(55)(70)$

8. A cable is attached 9 feet high on a wooden tent pole. The cable is anchored to the ground as shown. Which of the expressions could be used to find the length (l), in feet, of the cable?

(1) $\sqrt{9^2 + 8^2}$
(2) $\sqrt{9^2 - 8^2}$
(3) $\sqrt{9 + 8}$
(4) $9^2 - 8^2$
(5) $9^2 + 8^2$

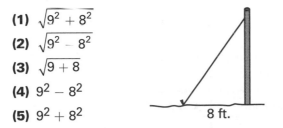

8 ft.

9. If the circumference (C) of a circle is known, which of the following formulas could be used to find the radius of the circle?

(1) $r = \dfrac{C\pi}{2}$
(2) $r = \dfrac{C}{2}$
(3) $r = \dfrac{C}{\pi}$
(4) $r = 2 \times \dfrac{C}{\pi}$
(5) $r = \dfrac{C}{2\pi}$

10. Melissa bought 3 dozen cake donuts for $15.12. Which of the following expressions could be used to find the cost of one donut?

(1) $15.12 \div 3$
(2) $15.12 \div 12$
(3) $15.12 \div 3(12)$
(4) 15.12×3
(5) 15.12×12

11. Gwen plans to borrow $9,000 to help pay for college. At the end of 5 years, she will owe the loan amount plus $1,350 in interest. If the loan is financed using simple interest, which equation could be used to find the interest rate Gwen is paying?

(1) $r = \$1,350(\$9,000)(5)$
(2) $r = \dfrac{\$9,000(5)}{\$1,350}$
(3) $r = \dfrac{\$1,350}{\$9,000(5)}$
(4) $r = \dfrac{\$1,350(5)}{\$9,000}$
(5) $r = \dfrac{\$9,000}{\$1,350(5)}$

12. The drawing below shows the floor plan for a large room. In the drawing, all corners of the room are right angles. Which of the following expressions could be used to find the perimeter of the room in feet?

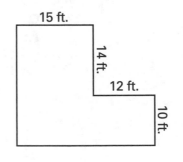

15 ft.

14 ft.

12 ft.

10 ft.

(1) $15(24) + 12(10)$
(2) $15(14) + 12(10)$
(3) $(24)(27)$
(4) $15 + 14 + 12 + 10$
(5) $24 + 15 + 14 + 12 + 10 + 27$

Answers and explanations start on page 89.

LOGICAL REASONING

We expect people to have a logical reason for what they do. In the same way, using logical reasoning to solve math problems means having a reason for each step that you take.

One way to use logic is to organize your thinking by making a chart. This is an important strategy for solving algebra word problems.

Sample Question

Lana is twice as old as her sister Allison. Four years ago, she was three times as old as Allison. How old is Allison now?

(1) 4   **(2)** 6   **(3)** 8   **(4)** 12   **(5)** 16

Think It Through

Q: To solve by writing an equation, what number should you assign the variable to?
A: Use the variable for the number that the problem tells you the least about. In this case, Allison's age. Then write expressions for the other numbers using the variable.

Q: How can you write an equation that includes all the information from the problem?
A: Make a chart showing the girls' ages now and the girls' ages 4 years ago. Write expressions for each box in the table.

	Allison's Age	Lana's Age
NOW	x	$2x$
4 YEARS AGO	$x - 4$	$2x - 4$

Refer back to the problem. Four years ago, Lana was three times as old as Allison, so Lana's age 4 years ago ($2x - 4$) is three times Allison's age 4 years ago, or $3(x - 4)$. Therefore, one way to write the equation is $2x - 4 = 3(x - 4)$.

Q: Solve the problem. Which answer choice is correct?
A: Choice 1 is Allison's age 4 years ago.
Choice 2 comes from solving the wrong equation.
Choice 3 is correct.
Choice 4 is Lana's age 4 years ago.
Choice 5 is Lana's age now.

Q: Does the answer make sense?
A: Yes. If Allison is 8 now, then Lana is 16. Four years ago, they were 4 and 12. Since 12 is three times 4, the answer works.

Answer and Explanation

(3) 8 Solve the equation:
$$2x - 4 = 3(x - 4)$$
$$2x - 4 = 3x - 12$$
$$8 = x$$

Go back to the chart to see what x stands for. The variable x represents Allison's age now, which is what the problem asked.

At first glance, some problems may not seem to have all the information you need. If an important fact is missing, it is sometimes possible to solve for that fact.

In the figure below, angles 1 and 4 are congruent. What is the measure of ∠4?

(1) 18°
(2) 40°
(3) 62°
(4) 80°
(5) 100°

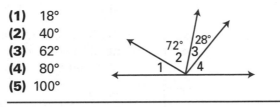

Think It Through

Q: What do you need to know to answer the question?
A: Since ∠1 and ∠4 are congruent, they have the same measure. If you know their total, you can divide by 2 to find the measure of ∠4. But the problem doesn't tell you their total.

Q: Can you find the missing information?
A: Yes. A straight angle or line is 180°. The total of ∠2 and ∠3 is 72° + 28° = 100°. Therefore, the sum of ∠1 and ∠4 must be 180° − 100° = 80°. You have what you need to solve the problem.

Answer and Explanation

(2) 40° Divide: 80° ÷ 2 = 40°. Both ∠1 and ∠4 measure 40°; therefore, choice 2 is correct.

Guided Practice

Use the hints to help you solve the problems, and explain your answers.

HINT: Work backwards from the question. What facts do you need to answer the question?

1. The area of the shaded section is 66 square inches. The perimeter of the larger rectangle is 50 inches. What is the area, in square inches, of the inner rectangle?

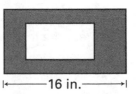

(1) 11   **(2)** 78   **(3)** 116   **(4)** 144   **(5)** 478

Answer _____ is correct because _____

_____

HINT: Ignore facts you don't need. If needed facts are missing, can you solve for them?

2. Tyra bought a shirt for $18.90. The total included 8% sales tax. What was the cost of the shirt before tax?

(1) $10.90   **(4)** $17.82
(2) $17.39   **(5)** $18.82
(3) $17.50

Answer _____ is correct because _____

_____

Answers and explanations start on page 90.

Choose the correct answer. Use the hints to help you solve the problems.

1. Rhonda has 36 coins, all nickels and dimes. The total value of the coins is $2.50. How many nickels does she have?

   THINK: Make a chart to solve this problem. Complete the chart below.

	NICKELS	DIMES
NUMBER OF COINS	x	$36 - x$
VALUES OF COINS	$0.05x$	

   (1) 10
   (2) 14
   (3) 18
   (4) 22
   (5) 25

2. If the sides of a square are each increased by 2 inches, the area of the square is <u>increased by</u> 40 square inches. How many inches does one side of the original square measure?

   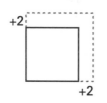

   +2

   +2

   THINK: How can you write an equation to express the information in the problem?

   (1) 8
   (2) 9
   (3) 10
   (4) 12
   (5) 18

3. The base of an isosceles triangle is 3 centimeters less than one of its legs. If the perimeter of the triangle is 21 centimeters, how many centimeters long is each leg?

   THINK: How can the properties of an isosceles triangle help you solve the problem?

   (1) 8
   (2) 9
   (3) 15
   (4) 16
   (5) Not enough information is given.

4. Matt drove 3 hours at an average speed of 65 miles per hour. Then he took a side road for 2 hours, driving at an average speed of 50 miles per hour. What was his average speed, in miles per hour, for the trip?

   THINK: To find the average speed, you will need to know the total distance. How can you find that out?

   (1) 23
   (2) 56
   (3) 57.5
   (4) 59
   (5) 62

5. A movie theater charges $9 for an adult's ticket and $5 for a child's ticket. The theater sold 240 tickets for a total of $1,968. How many children's tickets were sold?

   THINK: How can you express the number of both adult and children's tickets using the same variable? Make a chart to help.

	ADULTS	CHILDREN
NUMBER OF TICKETS		
VALUES OF TICKETS		

   (1) 8
   (2) 48
   (3) 192
   (4) 197
   (5) Not enough information is given.

6. The total of three consecutive odd numbers is 207. What is the greatest of the three numbers?

   THINK: Consecutive means the numbers are in order. How can you write expressions for each number? Let the first one equal x.

   (1) 67
   (2) 69
   (3) 70
   (4) 71
   (5) 73

Choose the one best answer to each question.

7. Brandee is five times the age of Blake. In only four years, she will be three times his age. How old is Brandee now?

(1) 4
(2) 8
(3) 12
(4) 15
(5) 20

8. The length of a rectangle is 12 feet less than three times its width. If the perimeter of the rectangle is 48 feet, what is its length in feet?

(1) 9
(2) 12
(3) 15
(4) 30
(5) 36

9. A small safe has eighty $10- and $20-bills. If the total value of the bills is $1,350, how many $20-bills are in the safe?

(1) 25
(2) 35
(3) 45
(4) 50
(5) 55

Question 10 refers to the following drawing.

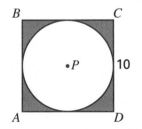

10. Circle *P* is inscribed inside square *ABCD*. What is the area, in square inches, of the shaded section? (**HINT:** What can the square tell you about the diameter of the circle?)

(1) 21.5
(2) 68.6
(3) 78.5
(4) 100
(5) Not enough information is given.

Questions 11 and 12 refer to this figure.

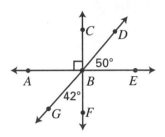

11. Line *AE* intersects line *CF* at point *B*. What is the measure of ∠*DBF*?

(1) 40°
(2) 50°
(3) 100°
(4) 140°
(5) Not enough information is given.

12. What is the measure of ∠*ABG*?

(1) 38°
(2) 48°
(3) 50°
(4) 92°
(5) 138°

13. Andre is 4 years older than Rhonda. Rhonda is three times as old as Jennifer. The total of their ages is 116 years. How old is Rhonda?

(1) 16
(2) 20
(3) 22
(4) 48
(5) 52

14. Triangle *ABC* has a perimeter of 35 inches. Side *AB* is 3 inches longer than side *AC*. Side *BC* is twice as long as side *AC*. How many inches long is side *AC*?

(1) 8
(2) 11
(3) 13
(4) 15
(5) 16

Answers and explanations start on page 90.

USE CALCULATORS WITH EXPRESSIONS

On the GED Mathematics Test, you will use a Casio *fx*-260 calculator. You can use it to evaluate expressions. You evaluate an expression when you substitute numbers for variables and perform the indicated operations.

To do algebra on a scientific calculator, you will need to use these keys:

$+/-$	change sign key
$[(-]$ and $-)]$	grouping symbol keys
x^2	square key
SHIFT x^2	square root $\sqrt{\ }$ (pressing SHIFT will access the 2nd function shown above the square key)
x^y	raise to any power key
$a^{b}/_{c}$	fraction key

Sample Question

What is the value of the expression $3ab - \sqrt{a + b}$ when $a = -2$ and $b = 6$?

(1) 38   **(2)** 36   **(3)** −34   **(4)** −36   **(5)** −38

Think It Through

Q: What operations are involved in this expression?
A: Multiplication, addition, subtraction, and finding a square root.

Q: Will any of these operations need to be placed in grouping symbols?
A: Yes, you need to add *a* and *b* before you take the square root of the sum. I don't need to group the product of 3*ab* because the calculator multiplies and divides before it adds and subtracts. Scientific calculators follow the order of operations.

Q: What key order should I use to find the value?
A: 3 $\times$ 2 $+/-$ $\times$ 6 $-$ $[(-]$ 2 $+/-$ $+$ 6 $-)]$ SHIFT x^2 $=$
    Notice how −2 is entered each time as 2 $+/-$.

Q: Solve the problem. Which answer choice is correct?
A: Choice 1 (38) is the value if you use 2 instead of −2.
Choice 2 (36) is the value of part of the expression if you use 2 instead of −2.
Choice 3 (−34) adds the square root instead of subtracting it.
Choice 4 (−36) is the value of part of the expression.
Choice 5 is correct.

Answer and Explanation

3 $\times$ 2 $+/-$ $\times$ 6 $-$ $[(-]$ 2 $+/-$ $+$ 6 $-)]$ SHIFT x^2 $=$ −38

The answer is **(5) −38**.

A calculator can be very helpful when you are working with formulas or equations involving difficult numbers. You can use the calculator to do parts of the equation. Be sure you follow the rules of algebra as you work towards a solution.

Sample Question

The cone shown at the right has a radius of 4 inches. What is the volume of the cone to the nearest cubic inch?

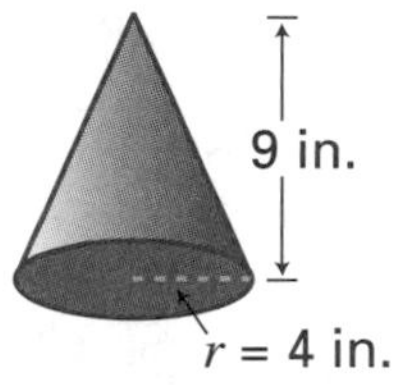

9 in.

r = 4 in.

(1) 18
(2) 38
(3) 81
(4) 151
(5) 452

Think It Through

Q: Is there a formula that can help you solve the problem?
A: Yes, the GED Formulas page shows the formula for finding the volume of a cone: Volume $= \frac{1}{3} \times \pi \times$ radius$^2 \times$ height.

Q: What operations and special keys will you need?
A: The only operation is multiplication. You will also need the fraction key and the square key. Use 3.14 for π. Use these key strokes:

1 $\boxed{a^{b}/_{c}}$ 3 $\boxed{\times}$ 3.14 $\boxed{\times}$ 4 $\boxed{x^2}$ $\boxed{\times}$ 9 $\boxed{=}$

Answer and Explanation

(4) 151 After entering the keystrokes above, the display reads 150.72, which rounds to 151 cubic inches.

Guided Practice

Use the hints and your calculator to help you solve the problems. List which operations and special keys you used.

HINT: Do you know how to read a fraction in the display window? Bars separate the parts of a fraction.
$\boxed{3 \, \lrcorner \, 1 \, \lrcorner \, 8} = 3\frac{1}{8}$

1. The length of a rectangle is $3\frac{3}{4}$ inches. Its width is $2\frac{3}{8}$ inches. What is the perimeter, in inches, of the rectangle?

(1) $6\frac{1}{8}$ **(2)** $7\frac{1}{2}$ **(3)** $8\frac{1}{2}$ **(4)** $8\frac{29}{32}$ **(5)** $12\frac{1}{4}$

Operations and special keys: _____

_____

HINT: Can the calculator help you solve this problem quickly? If not, use paper and pencil.

2. Every test in Lina's English class is worth 100 points. This term her grades are 74, 81, 76, 90, and 86. What is the mean of her test scores?

(1) 67.64   **(4)** 85
(2) 81   **(5)** 93
(3) 81.4

Operations and special keys: _____

_____

Answers and explanations start on page 90.

Use the hints and your calculator to help you solve the problems. Write the operations and special keys you used.

1. What is the value of the expression below when $x = 2$ and $y = -1$?

   $(2x - 5y)(3x + 6y)$

   THINK: Which operation is indicated by the parentheses?

   (1) -12
   (2) -9
   (3) 0
   (4) 108
   (5) $2{,}400$

2. What is the value of $\dfrac{-(-b + 3^2) - 3}{2b + 1}$ when $b = 2$?

   THINK: What is the value of the top of the fraction? What is the value of the bottom? Then simplify.

   (1) $-2\frac{1}{5}$
   (2) -2
   (3) $2\frac{1}{5}$
   (4) 3
   (5) $3\frac{4}{5}$

3. The area of triangle ABC is 13.5 square centimeters. What is the measure, in centimeters, of segment AD?

   THINK: Is there a formula that can help? What is another name for segment AD?

   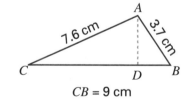

   $CB = 9$ cm

   (1) 1.4
   (2) 1.5
   (3) 3.0
   (4) 3.7
   (5) 3.9

4. Anthony borrowed $4,500 for 3 years. At the end of that time, he will owe $4,500 plus $1,620 in interest. Assume that Anthony financed the loan using simple interest. What interest rate did he pay on the loan?

   THINK: How will a percent appear on the calculator?

   (1) 3%
   (2) 12%
   (3) 27%
   (4) 36%
   (5) Not enough information is given.

5. Ryan is building the rectangular frame below to hold a large painting. He uses wire on the back to connect the opposite corners to keep the frame's corners at 90°. To the nearest inch, how long is each wire?

   THINK: What shapes are formed by the diagonals? Is there a formula you can use to find the length?

   (1) 44
   (2) 62
   (3) 90
   (4) 176
   (5) 1,920

6. What is the value of the expression below when $d = 2$ and $e = -3$?

   $\left(\dfrac{-4d}{-7 - e}\right)^3 + e^2$

   THINK: What should you do first in this expression? How should you apply the order of operations?

   (1) -17
   (2) -1
   (3) 1
   (4) $10\frac{3}{5}$
   (5) 17

Questions 7 and 8 refer to the figure below.

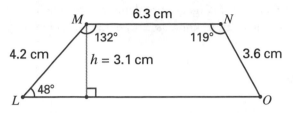

7. What is the measure of ∠NOL in the trapezoid?

(1) 132°
(2) 119°
(3) 90°
(4) 61°
(5) 48°

8. If the area of trapezoid *LMNO* is 26.66 square centimeters, what is the length, in centimeters, of side *LO*? (**HINT:** The two parallel sides in the figure are the bases.)

(1) 4.1
(2) 10.1
(3) 10.9
(4) 14.1
(5) 20.79

9. Mike rode his bike 9 kilometers due east and then rode 12 kilometers due south. How many kilometers is he from his starting point?

(1) 15
(2) 18
(3) 21
(4) 63
(5) 225

10. What is the value of the expression below when $x = -2$?

$$4x^3 + x^2 - 3x + 15$$

(1) 15
(2) −7
(3) −19
(4) −27
(5) −57

Question 11 refers to the drawing below.

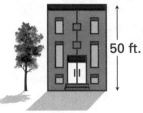

11. In the morning, the building casts a shadow that is 20 feet long. At the same time, the tree's shadow is 14 feet long. What is the height, in feet, of the tree?

(1) 28
(2) 30
(3) 34
(4) 35
(5) Not enough information is given.

12. Rory did three repair jobs last week. The second job paid $10 more than three times the first. The third job paid half as much as the second job. Altogether, she earned $675. How much was Rory paid for the second job?

(1) $120
(2) $185
(3) $215
(4) $235
(5) $370

13. The volume of a storage unit (shown below) is 192 cubic feet. How many feet long is the missing measurement?

(1) 8
(2) 16
(3) 19.2
(4) 32
(5) 48

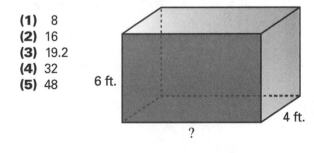

6 ft.

4 ft.

?

14. What is the value of $\dfrac{m + 5}{2(n - 3)}$, when $m = -3$ and $n = 4$?

(1) −27
(2) −0.5
(3) 1
(4) 4
(5) 5.5

Answers and explanations start on page 90.

Ten of the 50 items on the GED Mathematics Test will ask you to find an answer and enter it on a grid. Since the answers to algebra problems can be whole numbers, fractions, or decimals, you need to know how to enter each kind of number.

Follow these rules for entering answers:

- Write your answer in the row of boxes at the top. Put only one number or one symbol in each box.
- Fill in the correct circle below each box.
- If the answer is a mixed number, enter it as an improper fraction or decimal.

Sample Question

Building instructions call for three lengths of bolts. The large bolt is three times the length of the medium bolt. The medium bolt is two times the length of the small bolt. The total length of the bolts is $6\frac{3}{4}$ inches. How many inches long is the medium bolt?

Mark your answer on the grid.

Think It Through

Q: What is the best way to express each part of the problem?
A: Let x equal the length of the small bolt. The medium bolt will be $2x$, and the large bolt will be $3(2x)$. Set all three expressions equal to $6\frac{3}{4}$ if you want to use fractions or 6.75 if you want to use decimals.

Q: Write and solve the equation. What is your answer?
A:
$$x + 2x + 3(2x) = 6\frac{3}{4} \qquad\qquad x + 2x + 3(2x) = 6.75$$
$$9x = \frac{27}{4} \qquad\qquad 9x = 6.75$$
$$x = \frac{27}{4} \div 9 \qquad\qquad x = 6.75 \div 9$$
$$x = \frac{3}{4} \qquad\qquad x = 0.75$$

Solve for the medium bolt: $2x$.

$$2x = 2 \times \frac{3}{4} = \frac{6}{4}, \text{ or } \mathbf{1\frac{1}{2} \text{ inches}} \qquad 2x = 2 \times 0.75 = \mathbf{1.5 \text{ inches}}$$

**Answer and
Explanation**

Either of these grids is correct. Notice that $1\frac{1}{2}$ is entered as $\frac{3}{2}$, or 3/2.

GEOMETRY AND THE STANDARD GRID

Geometry problems often involve measurements. When you read a problem, the question will tell you the measurement unit to use. The answer you record on the grid must be in the unit of measure stated in the question.

Sample Question

Figure *EFGH* is a rectangle. What is the perimeter, in feet, of *EFGH*?

Mark your answer on the grid.

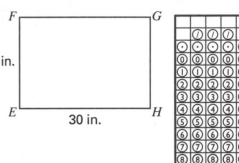

Think It Through

Q: What measurement unit does the problem use?
A: The drawing shows inches, but the question asks for feet.

Q: What do you need to do to answer the question?
A: You can use the perimeter formula to solve the problem in inches. Then change units to feet by dividing the number of inches by 12. Use the fact 1 foot = 12 inches.

Q: Do you need to change the way your answer is written to enter it?
A: After you divide by 12, you have an answer in feet with a remainder in inches. The remainder must be expressed as a fraction of a foot. Of course, you can also use a decimal to express the fraction.

Answer and Explanation

8.5 or 17/2 The perimeter is $2(30) + 2(21) = 102 \div 12 = 8$ feet 6 inches = 8.5, or $8\frac{1}{2}$ feet. If you want to enter the information using a fraction bar, you have to change $8\frac{1}{2}$ to the improper fraction $\frac{17}{2}$.

Guided Practice

Use the hints to help you solve the problems. Then enter your answers on the grids.

HINT: What unit label does problem 1 use? Read the question carefully.

HINT: In problem 2, will the answer be a whole number, a decimal, or a fraction? What is the best way to grid the answer?

1. The side of a square measures 375 cm. How would you write the measurement in meters? (**HINT:** 100 cm = 1 m)

Mark your answer on the grid.

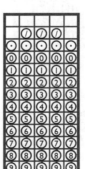

2. One number is $\frac{1}{3}$ of another number. The sum of the numbers is 84. What is the lesser of the two numbers?

Mark your answer on the grid.

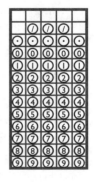

Answers and explanations start on page 91.

Use the hints to help you solve the problems. Mark your answers on the grids.

1. Last season, the Panthers won twice as many games as they lost. The difference between the games won and the games lost is 5. In simplest terms, what is the ratio of games won to games played?

THINK: Which operation does the word "difference" suggest?

4. In the equation below, what is the value of *x*?

$$-(x - 5) = 3x + 4$$

THINK: Is it easier for you to express the answer as a decimal or as a fraction?

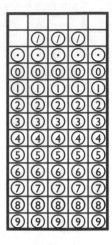

2. What is the area of the circle below to the nearest tenth inch?

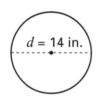

$d = 14$ in.

THINK: How can you find the radius when the diameter is known?

5. A rectangular swimming pool measures 15 meters by 11 meters. The owner plans to install a fence as shown below. How many meters of fencing will he need to surround the pool?

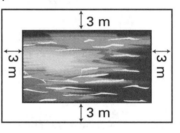

3 m
3 m
3 m
3 m

THINK: How can you calculate the measure of the sides of the fence?

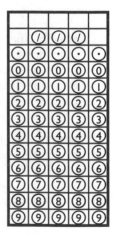

3. Barbara needs three different colors of fabric to make a costume. She needs three times as much blue as white, and half as much pale green as blue. If the total fabric needed is $9\frac{5}{8}$ yards, how many yards of white fabric will she need?

THINK: What are the rules for entering a mixed number on the grid?

6. The base of a parallelogram measures 3 feet 6 inches. The height measures 2 feet 6 inches. What is the area, in square feet, of the parallelogram?

THINK: How would you write 6 inches as a fraction or decimal?

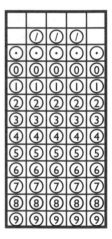

Solve. Mark your answers on the grids.

7. In the equation below, what is the value of x, when $y = -15$?

$$3x - 4y = 96$$

8. A cyclist averaged 8 mph going up a mountain trail and 20 mph coming down the same trail. If the cyclist covered a total of 24 miles, how many hours did the total trip up and back take? (**HINT:** Use the formula distance = rate × time.)

9. In centimeters, what is the perimeter of triangle *ABC* shown below?

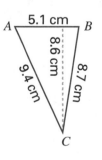

10. The perimeter of a rectangle is 10 meters. The length is 0.4 meter less than twice the width. What is the width, in meters, of the rectangle?

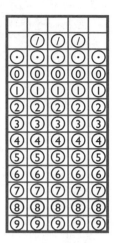

11. A beef roast weighs 78 ounces. What is the weight, in pounds, of the roast? (**HINT:** Use the fact 16 ounces = 1 pound.)

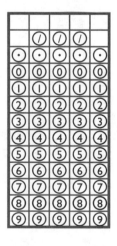

12. The average height of a group of four children is 4 feet 1 inch. If a fifth child is added to the group, the average height is 4 feet 2 inches. What is the height, in inches, of the fifth child?

Answers and explanations start on page 91.

PLOTTING POINTS

A coordinate plane is a system of marking a flat surface so that you can precisely locate any point on the surface. The coordinates of a point tell you how far the point is from the x- and y-axis.

A coordinate plane is usually drawn with intersecting lines, but the answer grid on the GED Mathematics Test is made up of circles. The rows and columns of circles represent the lines you are used to seeing. The x- and y-axis are marked with positive and negative numbers. Use the axes lines to locate points on the grid.

Sample Question

Of the points $(3, -1)$, $(2, -1)$ and $(0, -4)$, which point lies on the graph of the linear equation below?

$$y = 2x - 5$$

Mark your answer on the coordinate plane grid.

Think It Through

Q: How do you know when points are on the graph of a line?
A: Coordinates for a point are written in the order (x, y). Each pair of values for x and y that makes the equation true are points on the line.

Q: Which of the three points makes the equation true?
A: Check the points in the problem. Try each value for x and solve for y.

$(3, -1)$	$(2, -1)$	$(0, -4)$
$y = 2x - 5$	$y = 2x - 5$	$y = 2x - 5$
$\quad = 2(3) - 5$	$\quad = 2(2) - 5$	$\quad = 2(0) - 5$
$\quad = 1$	$\quad = -1$	$\quad = -5$
$-1 \neq 1$	$-1 = -1$	$-4 \neq -5$

Q: How do you plot the answer on the grid?
A: Use the x- and y-axes to locate the point. Start at positive 2 on the x-axis and move down 1 circle so that you are located in the row next to -1 on the y-axis.

Answer and Explanation

$(2, -1)$ Be sure to fill in the circle completely. Also, carefully erase any stray marks you may have made on the grid. The machine will score your answer as incorrect if it reads marks in more than one circle.

SLOPE AND DISTANCE BETWEEN POINTS

Slope is a ratio that tells you how steep a line is. The slope ratio compares rise (vertical change) to run (horizontal change). You can find the slope of a line if you know two points on the line. You can also measure the distance between two points on a line. Formulas for both these processes are on the GED Formulas page.

Sample Question

Line m passes through points A and B. What is the slope of line m? What is the distance between points A and B?

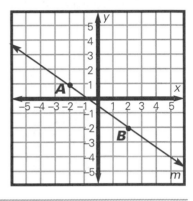

Think It Through

Q: What do I need to know to use the slope and distance formulas?

A: You need the coordinates for two points on the line. Let (x_1, y_1) equal point A at $(-2, 1)$ and let (x_2, y_2) equal point B at $(2, -2)$.

Q: Use the formulas to solve.

A: $\text{slope} = \dfrac{y_2 - y_1}{x_2 - x_1}$

$= \dfrac{(-2) - 1}{2 - (-2)}$

$= -\dfrac{3}{4}$

$\text{distance between points} = \sqrt{(x_2 - x_1)^2 + (y_2 - y_1)^2}$

$= \sqrt{[2 - (-2)]^2 + (-2 - 1)^2}$

$= \sqrt{4^2 + (-3)^2}$

$= \sqrt{16 + 9} = \sqrt{25} = 5$

Answer and Explanation

Slope $= -\dfrac{3}{4}$; distance $= 5$ units The slope means that for every 3 spaces the line goes down, it goes 4 spaces to the right. The distance is the measure of the diagonal between points A and B.

Guided Practice

Use the hints to help you solve the problems.

HINT: A midpoint is said to be midway between two points, in other words, an equal distance from each point.

HINT: In problem 2, does the slope you found make sense? Use the rise-over-run concept to check your work.

1. What point is located midway between $(-5, -3)$ and $(3, -3)$?

Mark your answer on the coordinate plane grid.

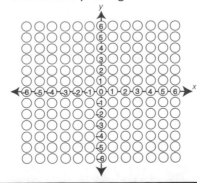

2. Point C at $(-3, -3)$ and point D at $(3, -1)$ lie on the graph of the line $3y = x - 6$. What is the slope of the line?

Mark your answer on the grid.

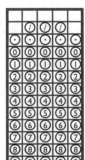

Answers and explanations start on page 92.

Use the hints to help you solve the problems. Mark your answer on the grids when provided.

1. Where is the point $(-2, 4)$ located on the coordinate plane?

THINK: Coordinates are written in the order (x, y).

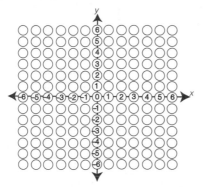

Question 2 is based on the following figure.

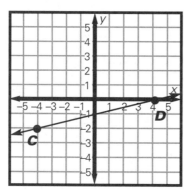

2. Which expression represents the distance from point C to point D?

THINK: Which point will be (x_1, y_1) and which will be (x_2, y_2)?

(1) $8^2 + 2^2$

(2) $(8 + 2)^2$

(3) $\sqrt{10}$

(4) $\sqrt{68}$

(5) $\sqrt{100}$

3. What point is located halfway between points $(2, -4)$ and $(2, 4)$ on a coordinate plane?

THINK: The points have the same x-coordinate. What does that tell you?

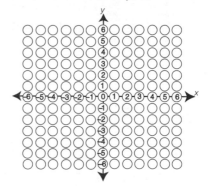

4. From the point of view of a hiker, a trail has an incline of $-\frac{1}{5}$. Which is true of the hill?

THINK: What do the parts of the slope ratio— rise and run—actually mean?

(1) For every 1 foot forward, the hiker goes up 5 feet.

(2) For every 1 foot forward, the hiker goes down 5 feet.

(3) For every 5 feet forward, the hiker goes up 1 foot.

(4) For every 5 feet forward, the hiker goes down 1 foot.

(5) For every 5 feet forward, the hiker goes down 5 feet.

5. What point is located on both the x- and y-axis?

THINK: How can the labels on the graph help you answer the question?

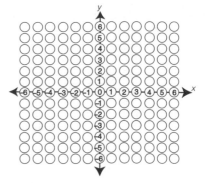

Solve. Mark your answers on the grids.

6. Point *A* is 5 units below (−1, 2). What are the coordinates of point *A*?

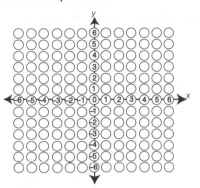

<u>Question 7</u> is based on the following figure.

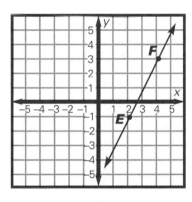

7. What is the slope of the line that passes through point *E* and point *F*?

8. What is the distance between point *Y* at (2, −3) and point *Z* at (−4, 5)?

9. A line segment is drawn from point *G* at (−1, 4) to point *H* at (5, 4). What point on the coordinate plane is the midpoint of the segment?

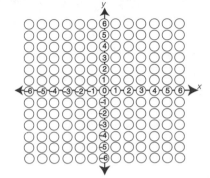

10. In the drawing below, the line shows the steepness of the staircase. What is the slope of the staircase?

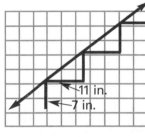

11 in.
7 in.

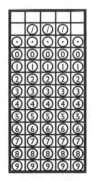

11. What is the distance between points *T* and *U* on the coordinate plane below?

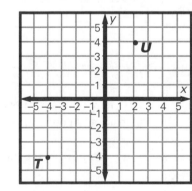

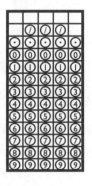

Answers and explanations start on page 92.

PLANE FIGURES

Some of the problems on the GED Mathematics Test may be about figures drawn on a coordinate plane. To solve these problems, you will need to think about the properties of the figure. Then use your reasoning to answer the question.

Sample Question

The coordinate plane shows the base of isosceles triangle *ABC*. At what point on the plane should you place point *C* so that the area of triangle *ABC* is 24 square units?

Mark your answer on the coordinate plane grid on the right.

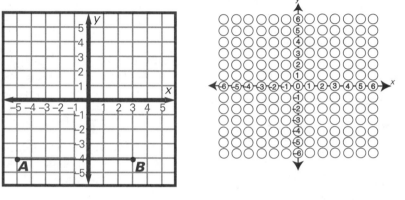

Think It Through

Q: What are the properties of an isosceles triangle?
A: An isosceles triangle has two equal sides and two equal angles. The equal angles are adjacent to the base.

Q: What information and operations are needed?
A: The problem refers to the area of a triangle. You can use the formula: Area $= \frac{1}{2} \times$ base $\times$ height. Count the units to find the length of the base (8 units). The area is 24 square units. You need to solve for the height.

Q: Solve the problem. Then record it on the grid.
A: Use the formula:

$$\text{Area} = \frac{1}{2} \times \text{base} \times \text{height}$$
$$24 = \frac{1}{2} \times 8 \times h$$
$$24 = 4 \times h$$
$$6 = h$$

The height is 6 units. Find the center of the base and count up 6 units.

Answer and Explanation

$(-1, 2)$ Fill in the circle completely.

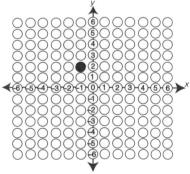

SLIDE, FLIP, AND ROTATE FIGURES

In the practical use of geometry, you sometimes need to describe the movement of a figure. Any figure can go through a progression of slides, flips, and rotations. A slide moves a figure to a new location on the grid. A flip reverses the figure, turning it over.

A rotation turns the figure around a designated point. To rotate a figure, remember that the point you are rotating around stays in the same place. A full circle equals 360°, so if you rotate a figure 360°, it is back where it started. A figure rotated 180° will face the opposite direction.

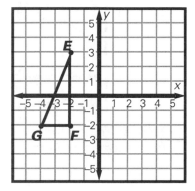

Sample Question

Triangle *EFG* is located on the coordinate plane as shown. Suppose it is flipped over the *y*-axis. What is the new location of point *G*?

Think It Through

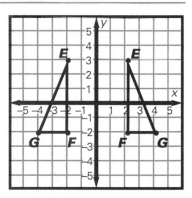

Q: What movement of the figure is required?
A: The figure must be flipped over the *y*-axis. The figure will be the same distance from the axis, but on the other side.

Q: Imagine or sketch the motion on scratch paper.
A: All the points have the same *y*-coordinates. Compare the figures. The *x*-coordinates are positive instead of negative.

Answer and Explanation

(4, −2) The new location of point *G* is at (4, −2). Notice that the figures are congruent even though they seem to be opposites.

Guided Practice

Use the hints to help you solve the problems, which are based on the figure below.

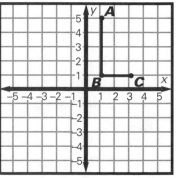

HINT: Do you need to move the figure to answer the question?

1. The figure shows two sides and three vertices of a rectangle. At what point would you place the final vertex (point *D*) to complete rectangle *ABCD*?

HINT: Point *B* does not move.

2. Suppose figure *ABC* is rotated 180° around point *B*. What is the new location of point *A*?

Answers and explanations start on page 92.

Use the hints to help you solve the problems. Mark your answers on the grids.

1. The figure drawn below is a circle. What is the location of the center of the circle?

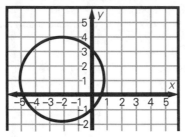

THINK: The center of a circle is equal distance from each point on the circle.

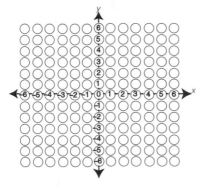

2. If triangle *PQR* is flipped over the *x*-axis, what will be the new location of point *Q*?

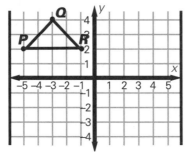

THINK: The flipped figure must be the same distance from the *x*-axis as the original figure.

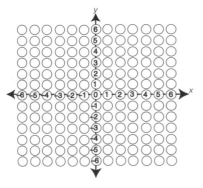

3. Two sides of figure *STUV* are shown below. If *STUV* is a parallelogram, at what location should point *V* be placed?

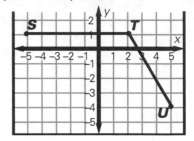

THINK: What are the properties of a parallelogram?

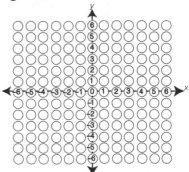

4. Figure *CDEF* is a square. Suppose you slide the figure 5 units up and 3 units to the right. What is the new location of point *D*?

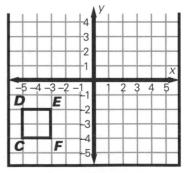

THINK: Concentrate on point *D*. Imagine moving it up and to the right.

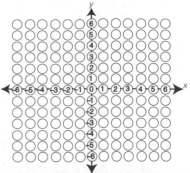

Solve. Mark your answers on the grids.

5. Triangle *XYZ* is rotated 270° around point *Z* in a clockwise direction around point *Z*. What is the new placement of point *X*? (**HINT:** 270° clockwise is the same as 90° counterclockwise.)

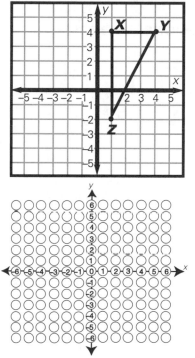

7. Figure *EFG* is an isosceles triangle. If you flip the figure over the *y*-axis, what will be the new location of point *F*?

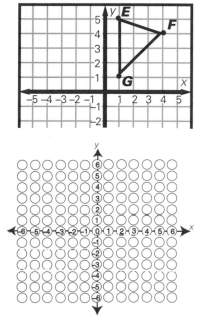

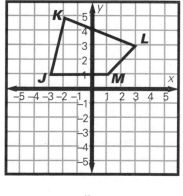

8. If figure *JKLM* is moved 6 units down and 2 units left, what is the new location of point *K*?

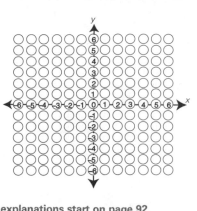

6. Trapezoid *ABCD* has two interior right angles. Where should you place *D* to complete the figure?

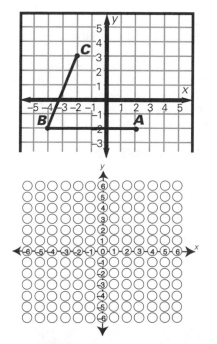

Answers and explanations start on page 92.

INTEGERS, PAGES 12–13

A.

1.	−6	6.	−31
2.	−25	7.	−5
3.	8	8.	2
4.	−3	9.	0
5.	−9		

B.

10.	−15	15.	−6
11.	80	16.	−3
12.	−15	17.	16
13.	147	18.	−40
14.	−21		

C.

19. **16** $4 - (-3)(+4) = 4 - (-12) = 4 + 12 = 16$

20. **–9**
$(-7) + \dfrac{(-5) + (+9)}{-2} = (-7) + \dfrac{4}{-2} = -7 + -2 = -9$

21. **–42** $2(-9 - 3) - 18 = 2(-12) - 18 = -24 - 18 = -42$

22. **4**
$\dfrac{-6(3 - 5)}{-12 + 15} = \dfrac{-6(-2)}{3} = \dfrac{12}{3} = 4$

23. **5** $2 - (-1)(3) = 2 - (-3) = 2 + 3 = 5$

24. **16** $(-16 + 12)(2 - 6) = (-4)(-4) = 16$

25. **23** $-7 - 3(4 - 9) + 15 = -7 - 3(-5) + 15 = -7 - (-15) + 15 = -7 + 15 + 15 = 23$

26. **1**
$\dfrac{-2(-5 + 10)}{-10} = \dfrac{-2(5)}{-10} = \dfrac{-10}{-10} = 1$

27. **–14** $15 - 22 - \dfrac{-14}{-2} = 15 - 22 - (+7) = -7 - 7 = -14$

D.

28. **(3) 42°** The temperature went up +10° (6° + 4°) from 8 A.M. to 10 A.M. It then went down 16° (−5° + −3° + −8°) from 10 A.M. to 1 P.M.
$48° + 10° - 16° = 42°$

29. **(3) (−8 + 9) − 15** Choice (3) is the only choice that shows −8 and 9 being added and then subtracting 15 from that total.

30. **(1) multiply −9 by 2** For this problem, work any operations in parentheses first.

POWERS AND ROOTS, PAGES 14–15

A.

1.	36	6.	64
2.	−8	7.	−1
3.	81	8.	5
4.	9	9.	64
5.	11		

B.

10.	between 7 and 8	12.	between 12 and 13
11.	between 10 and 11	13.	between 3 and 4

C.

14.	4	19.	54
15.	50	20.	50
16.	4	21.	14
17.	−8	22.	20
18.	115		

D.

23. **(5) $2(10^2) + 4^2$** $6^3 = 6 \times 6 \times 6 = 216$ and $2(10^2) + 4^2 = 2(100) + 16 = 200 + 16 = 216$

24. **(3) raise 3 to the fourth power** In this problem, find the value of the exponents first.

25. **(4) 170** The area of the first square is $A = 7^2$, and the area of the second square is $A = 11^2$. Total area: $7^2 + 11^2 = 49 + 121 = 170$ sq. in.

EXPRESSIONS, PAGES 16–17

A.

1.	D	4.	E
2.	A	5.	C
3.	B		

B.

6.	30	9.	54
7.	5	10.	−4
8.	10	11.	5

C.

12. **(5) 28** Substitute values and solve.
$5[4(-2) - 3(-4)] + (-2)(-4) = 5[-8 + 12] + 8 = 5(4) + 8 = 20 + 8 = 28$

13. **(4) 3x – $150** If Rick's salary = x, Anya's salary is three times that amount minus $150.

14. **(2) 2x + 2.5** Multiply the weight of Box B (x) by 2 and add 2.5.

SCIENTIFIC NOTATION, PAGES 18–19

A.

1.	1.3×10^4	4.	7.8×10^{-4}
2.	6.15×10^9	5.	8.52×10^{-9}
3.	5.6×10^6	6.	7.3×10^{-7}

B.

7.	1,500	10.	0.000049
8.	267,000	11.	0.00175
9.	800,000,000	12.	0.0000000028

C.

13. **(2) 5.8×10^{-5}** Move the decimal point to the right until you have a number between 1 and 10. Count the number of decimal places you moved, and write the exponent as a negative number.

14. **(1) 6.5×10^7** Write 65 million as 65,000,000. Then write the number in scientific notation.

15. **(1) Mars** Earth's diameter is $7.9 \times 10^3 = 7.9 \times 1,000 = 7,900$ miles. Mars has a diameter that is closest in size with a diameter of $4.2 \times 10^3 = 4.2 \times 1,000 = 4,200$ miles.

EQUATIONS, PAGES 20–21

A.

1.	$x = 12$	6.	$s = -7$
2.	$y = 5$	7.	$t = -100$
3.	$a = -8$	8.	$y = 16$
4.	$w = 31$	9.	$z = -9$
5.	$x = 10$	10.	$p = -17$

B.

11. **(2) 1.5w = $15** Set up an equation that multiplies Mike's wage by 1.5 and equals $15.

12. **(5) 310** Let d = the distance Kendra drove on the first day. Add 45 miles to d to equal the distance she drove on the second day (355). $d + 45 = 355$, so $d = 355 - 45 = 310$

13. **(3) −0.5** Solve for n.

$$\frac{-16}{n} = 32$$

$$\frac{(n)(-16)}{n} = 32n$$

$$\frac{-16}{32} = \frac{32n}{32}$$

$$-\frac{1}{2} = n, \text{ and } -\frac{1}{2} = -0.5$$

14. **(1) 95 + L = 120** Set up an equation that sets the sum of the missing length for the gate plus 95 feet equal to the total length of 120 feet.

MULTI-STEP EQUATIONS, PAGES 22–23

A.

1. $x = 2$ **6.** $z = 6$
2. $y = 60$ **7.** $x = 33$
3. $t = 3$ **8.** $y = -9$
4. $w = -14$ **9.** $p = 3$
5. $s = -5$ **10.** $z = -4$

B.

11. **(5) 15** $n = 60 - 3n$, $4n = 60$, so $n = 15$
12. **(2) 8** $28 = 3x + 4$, $24 = 3x$, so $x = 8$
13. **(3) x + (x + 20) = 120** Let x = the number of boys, and $x + 20$ = the number of girls who signed up. $x + (x + 20) = 120$
14. **(5) 140** Set up an equation. If $x + 10 + 2x = 220$, then $3x = 210$, and $x = 70$. Evaluate $2x$, the distance from Parker to Davis, by substituting the value 70 into the expression: $2x = 2(70) = 140$.

INEQUALITIES, PAGES 24–25

A.

1. $x \geq 19$ **4.** $b < -4$
2. $y < -1$ **5.** $n < 20$
3. $z \leq 7$ **6.** $w \leq 99$

B.

7. $x \leq 4$

8. $z > -6$

9. $y \leq 2$

10. $3 < w$

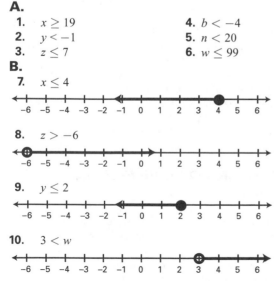

C.

11. **(3) x < −4** The graph shows an open circle, so −4 is not part of the solution, only values less than −4.

12. **(2) w ≥ $150** Matt needs to save $150 a month or more, so $150 is included in the solution.

13. **(2) n ≥ −3** Set up an inequality and solve. $3n - 4 \geq -13$, $3n \geq -9$, so $n \geq -3$

14. **(5) 4** Solve $x + 4 < 9$, so $x < 5$. Any number less than 5 is correct.

THE COORDINATE PLANE, PAGES 26–27

A.

1. $(-4, 3)$ **4.** $(1, 0)$
2. $(0, 5)$ **5.** $(4, -4)$
3. $(4, 1)$ **6.** $(-2, -4)$

B.

7.–12. See coordinate plane below.

C.

13. **(4) (−1, 2)** On the coordinate plane, 4 units to the left (x-coordinate) and 3 units up (y-coordinate) a point at $(3, -1)$ is $(-1, 2)$.

14. **(1) P** Move two units left along the x-axis and one unit up the y-axis.

15. **(2) in the upper-right section of the plane** Both coordinates are positive.

16. **(3) 0** Since the point is on the x-axis, the value of the y-coordinate is 0.

LINEAR EQUATIONS, PAGES 28–29

A.

1. Coordinate pairs: $(-2, -6)$, $(0, 0)$, $(2, 6)$
2. Coordinate pairs: $(-3, 6)$, $(0, 3)$, $(3, 0)$
3. Coordinate pairs: $(-2, 3)$, $(4, 6)$, $(6, 7)$

B.

The points graphed may vary, but the graphed lines should look the same. See the sample graph provided on the next page.

4.–6. refer to the graphed lines below.

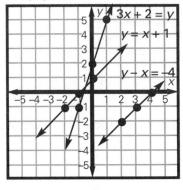

C.

7. **(3) Line c** Choose a couple of values for x and solve for y to find two points on the line. For example, if $x = 0$, $y = 2(0) + 5 = 5$, the coordinates are (1, 7). If $x = -2$, $y = 2(-2) + 5 = 1$, the coordinates are $(-2, 1)$. Line c is the graph of the equation $y = 2x + 5$.

8. **(4) $y = -x + 6$** Substitute the values into the equations. When both sides of the equation are equal, you have found the correct equation. For $y = -x + 6$, $y = -(-5) + 6 = 5 + 6 = 11$, which is the y-coordinate in $(-5, 11)$.

PATTERNS AND FUNCTIONS, PAGES 30–31

A.

1.	-7	**4.**	0.0625
2.	32	**5.**	27
3.	$\frac{1}{15}$	**6.**	13

B.

7. Function: $n = 4p$ Missing Number: 40
8. Function: $n = 3p + 1$ Missing Number: 76
9. Function: $n = 6p + 3$ Missing Number: 243

C.

10. **(3) \$1.56** Find the weight of 5.5 on the horizontal axis. Follow directly across to the vertical axis. The value is \$1.56.

11. **(4) $E = \$400 + 0.15s$** Add \$400 to 15% times his total sales ($0.15s$).

12. **(3) -27** Substitute 4 for p. $n = -8(4) + 5 = -32 + 5 = -27$

QUADRATIC EQUATIONS, PAGES 32–33

A.

1.	$x^2 + 10x + 21$	**3.**	$2x^2 + 3x - 5$
2.	$x^2 + 5x - 36$	**4.**	$x^2 - 20x + 96$

B.

5.	$x = 6$ and $x = -5$	**7.**	$x = -7$ and $x = -2$
6.	$x = 3$ and $x = 1$	**8.**	$x = -3$ and $x = 8$

C.

9. **(3) 2** Solve by substituting the values into the equation. $3(2^2) - 2(2) = 8$, $3(4) - 4 = 8$, $12 - 4 = 8$, so $8 = 8$

10. **(4) $(x - 5)$** Think about which factors of 40 add up to 13. Try 5 and 8. Since $13x$ is negative and 40 is positive, both factors will use a minus sign. $(x - 5)(x - 8)$

11. **(1) -4 and 12** Think about which factors of 48 have a difference of 8. Try 4 and 12. Since $8x$ is negative, use a minus sign with the greater factor: $(x + 4)(x - 12)$. The values that would make each factor equal 0 are -4 and 12.

12. **(5) $x^2 + x - 2$** Multiply the factors. $(x + 2)(x - 1) = x^2 - x + 2x - 2 = x^2 + x - 2$

13. **(3) 6** Think about which factors of 36 add up to 12. Try 6 and 6. Since $12x$ is negative and 36 is positive, use a minus sign in both factors. $(x - 6)(x - 6) = 0$. The equation has a solution of 6.

LINES AND ANGLES, PAGES 34–35

A.

1.	D	**4.**	C
2.	A	**5.**	E
3.	B		

B.

6. Complementary: 58°   **8.** Complementary: 75°
     Supplementary: 148°   Supplementary: 165°
7. Complementary: 14°
     Supplementary: 104°

C.

9. **(3) acute** Since $\angle COD$ is a right angle, you know that $\angle COA$ is a right angle. Since $\angle BOC$ is less than 90°, you know that it is an acute angle.

10. **(5) $\angle DOE$** Of the angles listed, only $\angle DOE$ shares a common side and vertex with $\angle COD$.

11. **(2) 60°** Use the fact that a straight angle equals 180°. $180° - 120° = 60°$

12. **(4) The angles are complementary.** Since the sum of the angles equals 90°, the angles are complementary.

TRANSVERSALS AND PARALLEL LINES, PAGES 36–37

A.

1. **a.** $m\angle 2 = 142°$ **2.** **a.** $m\angle 3 = 123°$
    b. $m\angle 3 = 38°$ **b.** $m\angle 5 = 123°$
    c. $m\angle 4 = 142°$ **c.** $m\angle 8 = 57°$

B.

3. **(5) lines s and t must be parallel** If $m\angle 2$ and $m\angle 6$ both equal 128°, they are corresponding angles. Therefore, lines s and t must be parallel.

4. **(4) $\angle 5$ and $\angle 8$** These angles are vertical angles and therefore have the same measure.

5. **(5) $\angle 8$** Of the angles listed, only $\angle 8$ shares a common side and vertex with $\angle 5$.

6. **(3) $\angle 5$ and $\angle 7$** Since $\angle 7$ is a corresponding angle to $\angle 3$, and $\angle 5$ is a vertical angle to $\angle 7$, they both have a measure of 96°.

TRIANGLES AND QUADRILATERALS, PAGES 38–39

A.

1.	parallelogram	**3.**	isosceles triangle
2.	square	**4.**	obtuse triangle

B.

5.	parallelogram	**7.**	rectangle
6.	equilateral triangle	**8.**	right triangle

C.

9. **(3) right** Since the sum of the angles in a triangle = 180°, the remaining angle is 90°, making it a right triangle.

10. **(5) trapezoid** A quadrilateral with only one pair of parallel sides is a trapezoid.

11. **(3) the measure of the angles** You need to know if the four angles are right angles, otherwise the figure could be a rhombus.

12. **(3) 145°** In a rhombus, opposite angles are equal, and the sum of the angles in a quadrilateral is 360°. Set up an equation and solve for x.

$$35° + 35° + x + x = 360°$$
$$70° + 2x = 360°$$
$$2x = 290°$$
$$x = 145°$$

PERIMETER, PAGES 40–41

A.

1.	22 cm	**4.**	92 mm
2.	68.8 in.	**5.**	6.7 cm
3.	15 in.	**6.**	8 in.

B.

7. **(2) 15 × 3** A triangle with three equal angles also has three equal sides, so multiply the length of one side by three to find the perimeter.

8. **(3) 30** Add the lengths to find the perimeter. $4.5 + 6 + 4.5 + 4.5 + 6 + 4.5 = 30$ ft.

9. **(5) 104** You can add four inches to each width and length and add the four lengths together: $24 + 28 + 24 + 28 = 104$ inches.

10. **(3) 27.2** A rhombus has four equal sides. Multiply the length of one side by four. $6.8 \times 4 = 27.2$ centimeters

AREA, PAGES 42–43

A.

1.	2,800 cm²	**4.**	480 cm²
2.	25 sq. ft.	**5.**	12 sq. in.
3.	172.5 sq. in.	**6.**	18 sq. ft.

B.

7. **(1) 20** Use the width of the rectangle for the height of the triangle since the side of the rectangle forms a 90° angle with the base. Find the area of the triangle using the area formula $A = \frac{1}{2}bh = \frac{1}{2}(10)(4) = 20$ cm².

8. **(5) $\sqrt{64}$** Since the formula for area of a square is $A = s^2$, find the square root of the area to determine the value of s.

9. **(2) 14** Use the area formula for a rectangle, and substitute the known values for the variables. $A = lw$
$$126 = 9l$$
$$\frac{126}{9} = l$$
$$14 = l$$

10. **(2) 324** Since you are given the measures for the base and height of a triangular figure, you can find the area. $A = \frac{1}{2}bh = \frac{1}{2}(18)(36) = 324$ sq. in.

VOLUME, PAGES 44–45

A.

1.	64 cubic inches	**4.**	360 cubic inches
2.	175 cubic feet	**5.**	729 cubic inches
3.	480 cubic inches	**6.**	13.75 centimeters cubed

B.

7. **(4) 247.5** Find the area of the base (length × width), and multiply by the height.
Volume = $7.5(3)(11) = 247.5$ cu. in.

8. **(4) $\frac{1}{2} \times 5 \times 8 \times 9$** First find the area of a side.
$A = \frac{1}{2}bh = \frac{1}{2} \times 8 \times 5$. Then use this area to find the volume of the container.
Volume = area of side × height = $\frac{1}{2} \times 8 \times 5 \times 9$.

9. **(3) 50** Volume of the first box = $lwh = 6(3)(3) = 54$ cu. ft. Volume of the second box = $lwh = 4(0.5)(2) = 4$ cu. ft. Subtract to find the difference. $54 - 4 = 50$ cu. ft.

10. **(2) 8** Use the volume formula, and substitute the known measures for the variables. Find h, the height of the block.
$$V = lwh$$
$$128 = 16h$$
$$\frac{128}{16} = h$$
$$8 = h$$

CIRCLES, PAGES 46–47

A.

1. $C = 25.12$ in.
$A = 50.24$ sq. in.

2. $C = 6.28$ ft.
$A = 3.14$ sq. ft.

3. $C = 62.8$ mm
$A = 314$ mm²

B.

4. $V = 226.08$ cu. in.
5. $V = 57.88$ cm³
6. $V = 678.24$ cu. in.

C.

7. **(2) 25.12** Since the radius is 4 feet, the diameter is 2(4), or 8 feet. Use the formula for finding the circumference of a circle. $C = \pi d = 3.14(8) = 25.12$ feet

8. **(4) 16** Area of tree: $\pi r^2 = 3.14(2^2) = 12.56$ sq. ft. Area of border and tree: $\pi r^2 = 3.14(3^2) = 28.26$ sq. ft. Subtract to find the area of the border:
$28.26 - 12.56 = 15.7$ sq. ft., which rounds to 16 sq. ft.

9. **(2) 62.8** $C = \pi d = 3.14(20) = 62.8$ in.

10. **(4) 307.72** Since the diameter of the disk is 20, the radius is 10. Area of disk: $A = \pi r^2 = 3.14(10^2) = 314$ sq. in. Each hole has a diameter of 1 inch and a radius of 0.5. Find the area of one 1-inch hole: $A = \pi r^2 = 3.14(0.5^2) = 0.785$ sq. in. The area of 8 holes would be $8 \times 0.785 = 6.28$ sq. in. Subtract to find the remaining area of the metal disk: $314 - 6.28 = 307.72$ sq. in.

IRREGULAR FIGURES, PAGES 48–49

A.

1. $P = 16$ cm (missing measure = 2.5 cm)
2. $P = 64$ ft. (missing measure = $10 - 4 = 6$ ft.)
3. $P = 137.1$ in. (missing measure: half of the circumference of the whole circle; $C = \pi d = 3.14(30) = 94.20$; half of $C = 94.2 \div 2 = 47.1$)

B.

4. $A = 35$ **cm**^{2} Square: $A = s^2 = 5^2 = 25$ and triangle: $A = \frac{1}{2}bh = \frac{1}{2}(5)(4) = 10$; Add to find the total: $25 + 10 = 35$ cm^2

5. $A = 1{,}512$ **sq. yd.** Rectangle 1: $A = lw = 30(24) = 720$ sq. yd. Rectangle 2 has two missing measures. Missing length: $60 - 24 - 30 = 6$ yd. Missing width: $30 - 18 = 12$ or $24 - 12 = 12$ yd. Rectangle 2: $A = lw = 6(12) = 72$ sq. yd. Rectangle 3: $A = lw = 30(24) = 720$ sq. yd. Total area: $720 + 72 + 720 = 1{,}512$ sq. yd.

6. **63.25 sq. in.** Area of triangle: $A = \frac{1}{2}bh = \frac{1}{2}(8)(6) = 24$ sq. in. and area of circle: $A = \pi r^2 = 3.14(5^2) = 78.5$, so area of a half circle: $78.5 \div 2 = 39.25$ sq. in. Total area: $24 + 39.25 = 63.25$ sq. in.

C.

7. **(4) 400** Find any missing lengths: $30 - 20 = 10$ and $40 + 40 + 10 = 90$ and $90 - 70 = 20$; Add the lengths: $P = 70 + 10 + 20 + 50 + 40 + 40 + 30 + 10 + 20 + 20 + 40 + 50 = 400$ ft.

8. **(4) 108.9** One possible way to solve for the area is shown below. Area of each isosceles triangle is $A = \frac{1}{2}bh = \frac{1}{2}(11)(4.4) = 24.2$. Area of the parallelogram is $bh = 11(5.5) = 60.5$. Add to find the total: $24.2 + 24.2 + 60.5 = 108.9$ sq. yd.

CONGRUENT FIGURES, PAGES 50–51

A.

1. Yes, the figures are congruent based on the ASA rule.
2. No, the figures are not congruent since only one angle is congruent.
3. No, the figures are not congruent. Only one side is congruent, and no angles are congruent.
4. No, the figures are not congruent. Even though all three angles are congruent, that is not one of the rules that states what makes two triangles congruent.

B.

5. **(3) The triangles are congruent because of the ASA rule.** Since the angles of both triangles are congruent, and they have a corresponding side that is congruent, the angle-side-angle (ASA) rule applies.
6. **(2) LN** Name the side that is opposite the 20° angle.
7. **(1) SAS** You know the length of two corresponding sides is 10, two corresponding angles are right angles, and they share a common side. The side-angle-side (SAS) rule shows the triangles are congruent.
8. **(5) the length of side TU** You need to know the length of one side of square *TUVW*.

SIMILAR FIGURES, PAGES 52–53

A.

1. No, the figures are not similar because they don't have the same shape.
2. No, the figures are not similar because the ratios of corresponding lengths are not equal.
3. Yes, the figures are similar because the ratios of corresponding lengths are equal, and the angles are equal.
4. Yes, the figures are similar and congruent because the corresponding sides are equal in length.

B.

5. **(1) side AE** Look for the side that is the base of the other triangle.
6. **(3) 15** Set up a proportion using corresponding sides. Note that the base of $\triangle ABC$ is $15 + 10 = 25$.
$\frac{15}{25} = \frac{9}{x}$
$225 = 15x$
$15 = x$
7. **(2) 40** Write a proportion comparing height to shadow.
$\frac{6}{4.5} = \frac{x}{30}$
$180 = 4.5x$
$40 = x$
8. **(5) Circles O and P are congruent.** Since the radius of a circle is half its diameter, the radius of circle *P* is also 4 inches. Since the circles have the same shape and size, the circles are congruent.

PYTHAGOREAN RELATIONSHIP, PAGES 54–55

A.

1.	Yes	**5.**	No
2.	No	**6.**	No
3.	Yes	**7.**	Yes
4.	Yes	**8.**	No

B.

9. **(4)** $\sqrt{4{,}100}$ Draw a sketch of the problem. With Lake City being due north of Midtown and Bountiful being due east of Midtown, they form a right angle. The distance from Lake City to Bountiful would be the hypotenuse.
$c^2 = a^2 + b^2$
$c^2 = 50^2 + 40^2$
$c^2 = 2{,}500 + 1{,}600$
$c^2 = 4{,}100$
$c = \sqrt{4{,}100}$
10. **(2) 7** The brace is the hypotenuse, and the wall is one of the legs.
$c^2 = a^2 + b^2$
$25^2 = 24^2 + b^2$
$625 = 576 + b^2$
$49 = b^2$
$7 = b$
11. **(3)** $6^2 + 10^2 = c^2$ A rectangle has four right angles. By dividing the rectangle with a diagonal, two right triangles are formed with legs measuring 6 and 10. Use the known values in the formula for the Pythagorean Relationship.
12. **(5) The hypotenuse is longer than either leg.** The hypotenuse is always the longest side because it is across from the largest angle (90°).

WORD PROBLEMS, PAGES 56–59
GUIDED PRACTICE

1. **(1) 63** Answer 1 is correct because the number of installers should be between $\frac{1}{4}$ and $\frac{1}{3}$ of all employees.
2. **(5) Not enough information is given.** Answer 5 is correct because even though you can find the amount for 2 months, you can't find the amount for November alone.

GED SKILL BUILDER PRACTICE 1

1. **(2) 6** Let x = the number of chicken salads. Let $3x$ = the number of garden salads.
   $x + 3x = 24$
   $4x = 24$
   $x = 6$

2. **(5) Not enough information is given.** An isosceles triangle has two equal angles. You need to know if the angle measure given is for the third angle or one of the congruent angles.

3. **(3) $1.00** Find the amount of the raise. 8% = 0.08 and $12.50 × 0.08 = $1.00

4. **(3) 100°** $\angle 1$ and $\angle 5$ are corresponding angles, and $\angle 5$ and $\angle 8$ are supplementary angles.
   $180° - 80° = 100°$

5. **(2) 300** First, divide how much Spencer was paid by the amount per mile to find the total number of miles traveled: $126 ÷ $0.28 = 450 miles. Let x = second trip miles and $2x$ = first trip miles
   $x + 2x = 450$
   $3x = 450$
   $x = 150$ and $2x = 2(150) = 300$

6. **(4) $\angle DFE$** $\angle BFD$ is a right angle, which equals 90°, and $\angle AFE$ is a straight angle, which equals 180°. Therefore, the remaining two angles equal $180° - 90° = 90°$. Therefore, the two remaining angles are complementary.

7. **(3) $588** Multiply the monthly cost by the number of months in a year. Then add the product of four times the cost of one class. $39(12) + 4($30) = $588

8. **(5) the height of the barrel** The formula for volume of a cylinder is $V = \pi r^2 h$. Since you know the radius, you need the height.

9. **(1) 12** Let w = width and $2w - 5$ = length. Perimeter = $w + w + l + l$.
   $w + w + 2w - 5 + 2w - 5 = 62$
   $6w - 10 = 62$
   $6w = 72$
   $w = 12$

10. **(4) 288** Set up a proportion comparing pages to minutes.
    $\frac{50 \text{ pg.}}{60 \text{ min.}} = \frac{240 \text{ pg.}}{x \text{ min.}}$
    $60 × 240 ÷ 50 = 288$ minutes

11. **(4) They are congruent.** Vertical angles have equal measure, or they are congruent.

12. **(5) Not enough information is given.** Since the lines are not parallel, you do not know the measure of $\angle 5$, $\angle 6$, or $\angle 7$.

13. **(1) 26** Let x = Lamar, $2x$ = Carla, and $2x + 4$ = Jesse.
    $x + 2x + 2x + 4 = 134$
    $5x + 4 = 134$
    $5x = 130$
    $x = 26$

14. **(2) 13** Divide the number of students by the number of students per classroom: $224 ÷ 18 = 12.4$. The school would need a minimum of 13 classrooms to average 18 or fewer students per class.

FORMULAS AND EQUATIONS, PAGES 60–63
GUIDED PRACTICE

1. **Answer (3)** is correct because it multiplies 5 by 3 and adds that amount to 2 times 4.

2. **Answer (2)** is correct because it multiplies the side of the square by itself. $7 × 7 = 7^2$

GED SKILL BUILDER PRACTICE 2

1. **(1)** $w = \frac{204}{12}$ Use the formula for area of a rectangle, and substitute the known values.
   $A = lw$
   $204 = 12w$
   $\frac{204}{12} = w$

2. **(3)** $\frac{86 + 88 + p}{3}$ To find the average test score, you would add the three test scores and divide by the number of tests.

3. **(4) 5(4.2)(3.5)** The volume of a rectangular solid is $V = lwh = 5(4.2)(3.5)$.

4. **(2) $600(2)(0.05) + $600** You need to find the amount of simple interest and add that to the original amount. The rate of 5% = 0.05. Find the simple interest: $i = prt = $600(2)(0.05)$. Add the interest to $600 to find the amount to be paid back.

5. **(5)** $\frac{2(19.55)}{8.5}$ Use the area formula since height is one of the variables.
   $A = \frac{1}{2}bh$
   $19.55 = \frac{1}{2}(8.5)h$
   $2(19.55) = 8.5h$
   $\frac{2(19.55)}{8.5} = h$

6. **(1)** $t = \frac{1,430}{65}$ Use the distance formula, and plug in the known values.
   $d = rt$
   $1,430 = 65t$
   $\frac{1,430}{65} = t$

7. **(2) 3(70) + 2(55)** Use the formula distance = rate × time, but be sure to multiply the two different rates separately and then add. Multiply 3 hours by 70 mph and 2 hours by 55 mph, and then add.

8. **(1)** $\sqrt{9^2 + 8^2}$ You know the measures of both legs of the right triangle formed by the tent pole and ground. Use the Pythagorean formula $a^2 + b^2 = c^2$. You know the values for a and b, so find the square root to find the value of c.

9. **(5)** $r = \frac{C}{2\pi}$ The formula for circumference is $C = \pi d = 2\pi r$. Solve for the radius by dividing both sides of the equation by 2π.

10. **(3) $15.12 ÷ 3(12)** Divide the cost of the donuts by the number of donuts, in this case, 3 dozen, or $3 × 12$.

11. **(3)** $r = \frac{\$1,350}{\$9,000(5)}$ The formula for simple interest is $i = prt$. Fill in the known values, and solve for r (the rate).
    $i = prt$
    $\$1,350 = \$9,000(5)r$
    $\frac{\$1,350}{\$9,000(5)} = r$

12. **(5) 24 + 15 + 14 + 12 + 10 + 27** Find the perimeter by adding the lengths of the sides. Use the given measurements to find the missing lengths: $15 + 12 = 27$ and $14 + 10 = 24$.

PROBLEM SOLVING, PAGES 64–67
GUIDED PRACTICE

1. **Answer (2)** is correct because the area of the inner rectangle is the result of subtracting the area of the shaded portion from the entire area.

2. **Answer (3)** is correct because $17.50 plus 8% of $17.50 equals $18.90.

GED SKILL BUILDER PRACTICE 3

1. **(4) 22** Finish filling in the chart by giving dimes the value of $0.10(36 − x)$. Then add the value of the coins and set it equal to $2.50.
    $0.05x + $0.10(36 − x) = $2.50
    $0.05x + $3.60 − $0.10x = $2.50
    $3.60 − $0.05x = $2.50
    −$0.05x = −$1.10
    $x = 22$

2. **(2) 9** Use the formula for area of a square, $A = s^2$. Substitute values based on information in the problem.
    $A = s^2$
    $s^2 + 40 = (s + 2)^2$
    $s^2 + 40 = (s + 2)(s + 2)$
    $s^2 + 40 = s^2 + 4s + 4$
    $36 = 4s$
    $9 = s$

3. **(1) 8** Let the two legs = x and the base = $x − 3$.
    $x + x + x − 3 = 21$
    $3x − 3 = 21$
    $3x = 24$
    $x = 8$

4. **(4) 59** First find the total distance by multiplying each rate by its time: $3 \times 65 = 195$ and $2 \times 50 = 100$, so $195 + 100 = 295$ miles.
    Divide total miles by the total number of hours.
    $295 ÷ 5 = 59$ mph

5. **(2) 48** Fill in x for the number of adults' tickets and $240 − x$ for the number of children's tickets. Assign the value for adults' tickets as $9x$ and children's as $5(240 − x)$. Set up an equation and solve.
    $9x + $5(240 − x) = $1,968
    $9x + $1,200 − $5x = $1,968
    $4x = $768
    $x = 192$ So the number of children's tickets sold is $240 − 192 = 48$.

6. **(4) 71** Let the expressions for the three numbers equal x, $x + 2$, and $x + 4$.
    $x + x + 2 + x + 4 = 207$
    $3x + 6 = 207$
    $3x = 201$
    $x = 67$ So the greatest of the three numbers is $67 + 4 = 71$.

7. **(5) 20** Let Blake's age now = x and Brandee's age now = $5x$. For four years from now, let Blake's age = $x + 4$ and Brandee's age = $5x + 4$. Set Brandee's age four years from now equal to three times Blake's age four years from now.
    $5x + 4 = 3(x + 4)$
    $5x + 4 = 3x + 12$
    $2x = 8$
    $x = 4$ So Brandee's age now is $5(4) = 20$.

8. **(3) 15** Let the width = w and the length = $3w − 12$. Use the formula for perimeter of a rectangle:
    $P = 2 \times$ length $+ 2 \times$ width
    $48 = 2(3w − 12) + 2w$
    $48 = 6w − 24 + 2w$
    $72 = 8w$
    $9 = w$ Rectangle's length is $3(9) − 12 = 27 − 12 = 15$.

9. **(5) 55** Let the number of $10-bills = x and the number of $20-bills = $80 − x$. Let the value of the bills equal $10x$ and $20(80 − x)$. Write an equation that adds the value of the bills and sets the sum equal to $1,350.
    $10x + $20(80 − x) = $1,350
    $10x + $1,600 − $20x = $1,350
    −$10x = −$250
    $x = 25$ The number of $20-bills is $80 − 25 = 55$.

10. **(1) 21.5** The side of the square equals the diameter of the circle. Remember that the radius equals $\frac{1}{2}$ the diameter.
    Area of the square $= s^2 = 10^2 = 100$
    Area of the circle $= A = \pi r^2 = \pi(5)^2 = 78.5$
    The area of the shaded section is $100 − 78.5 = 21.5$.

11. **(4) 140°** $\angle ABC$ and $\angle FBE$ are vertical angles. Since $\angle ABC = 90°$, $\angle FBE = 90°$. Add the measures of $\angle FBE$ and $\angle DBE$: $50° + 90° = 140°$.

12. **(2) 48°** $\angle ABF$ is a right angle, so $\angle ABG$ is $90° − 42° = 48°$.

13. **(4) 48** Let Jennifer = x, Rhonda = $3x$ and Andre = $3x + 4$.
    $x + 3x + 3x + 4 = 116$
    $7x + 4 = 116$
    $7x = 112$
    $x = 16$ Rhonda's age is $3(16) = 48$.

14. **(1) 8** Let side $AC = x$, side $AB = x + 3$, and side $BC = 2x$. Write an equation to set the sum of the sides equal to the perimeter.
    $x + x + 3 + 2x = 35$
    $4x + 3 = 35$
    $4x = 32$
    $x = 8$

THE CASIO *fx*-260 CALCULATOR, PAGES 68–71
GUIDED PRACTICE

1. **(5) $12\frac{1}{4}$** Add using the fraction key, or multiply the mixed numbers by 2 and add.

2. **(3) 81.4** Add the scores, press the equals sign to get the total, and divide by 5. Or add the scores using the parentheses key and then divide.

GED SKILL BUILDER PRACTICE 4

1. **(3) 0** The parentheses show multiplication. Use the parentheses keys and the change sign key. Enter the keys in this order: $(2 \times 2 − 5 \times 1 +/−) \times (3 \times 2 + 6 \times 1 +/−) =$. Note that a number multiplied by $0 = 0$.

2. **(2) −2** The value of the top part of the fraction is −10, and the bottom value is 5. Divide −10 by $5 = −2$.

3. **(3) 3.0** Use the formula for area of a triangle. Segment AD is the height.
    $A = \frac{1}{2}bh$
    $13.5 = \frac{1}{2}(9)(h)$
    $27 = 9h$
    $3 = h$

4. **(2) 12%** The percent will appear as a decimal on the calculator. Use the simple interest formula.

$i = prt$

$\$1,620 = \$4,500(3)(r)$

$\dfrac{\$1,620}{\$4,500(3)} = r$

$r = 0.12 = 12\%$

5. **(2) 62** The diagonals form the hypotenuses of congruent right triangles. Use the Pythagorean formula $c^2 = a^2 + b^2 = 48^2 + 40^2 = 3,904$. Find the square root using the SHIFT x^2 keys. The hypotenuse $c = 62.48$, rounds to 62.

6. **(5) 17** Find the value of the top number and bottom number separately, then divide as indicated by the fraction bar. Then raise the value to the third power and add -3^2.

$\left(\dfrac{-8}{-4}\right)^3 + (-3)^2 = 2^3 + 9 = 17$

7. **(4) 61°** The sum of the angles in a quadrilateral equal 360°. Use the parentheses keys to solve:

$360° - (48° + 132° + 119°) = 61°$.

8. **(3) 10.9** Use the formula for area of a trapezoid, and substitute the known values.

$A = \dfrac{1}{2} \times (b_1 + b_2) \times h$

$26.66 = \dfrac{1}{2} \times (6.3 + b_2) \times 3.1$

$26.66 \times 2 \div 3.1 - 6.3 = b_2$

$10.9 = b_2$

You could also substitute the different answer choices in the equation until you found the correct one.

$26.66 = \dfrac{1}{2} \times (6.3 + 10.9) \times 3.1$

9. **(1) 15** The directions Mike rode formed a right triangle. The direct distance between his starting and stopping points can be found by using the Pythagorean formula:

$c^2 = a^2 + b^2$

$c^2 = 9^2 + 12^2$

$c^2 = 225$

$c = 15$

10. **(2) −7** Use the following calculator keys:

$4\ \boxed{\times}\ \boxed{[(-)}\ 2\ \boxed{+/-}\ \boxed{x^2}\ 3\ \boxed{-)]}\ \boxed{+}\ 2\ \boxed{+/-}$

$\boxed{x^2}\ \boxed{-}\ 3\ \boxed{\times}\ 2\ \boxed{+/-}\ \boxed{+}\ 15\ \boxed{=}$.

The result is −7.

11. **(4) 35** Set up a proportion comparing actual height to length of shadow. $\dfrac{50\text{ ft.}}{20\text{ ft.}} = \dfrac{x\text{ ft.}}{14\text{ ft.}}$

$50 \times 14 \div 20 = 35$ ft.

12. **(5) $370** Let the first job's pay $= x$, the second $= 3x + \$10$, and the third $= 0.5(3x + \$10)$.

$x + 3x + \$10 + 1.5x + \$5 = \$675$

$5.5x + \$15 = \$675$

$5.5x = \$660$

$x = \$120$ So Rory paid $3(\$120) + \$10 = \$370$ for the second job.

13. **(1) 8** Use the formula for finding the volume of a rectangular solid.

$V = lwh$

$192 = l(4)(6)$

$\dfrac{192}{24} = l$

$8 = l$

14. **(3) 1** Find the values of the numerator and denominator first, and then divide. $\dfrac{-3 + 5}{2(4 - 3)} = \dfrac{2}{2} = 1$

THE STANDARD GRID, PAGES 72–75
GUIDED PRACTICE

1. **3.75** Divide the number of centimeters by 100 to find the value in meters. $375 \div 100 = 3.75$ m

2. **21** Let one number $= x$ and the other $= \dfrac{1}{3}x$.

$x + \dfrac{1}{3}x = 84$

$\dfrac{4}{3}x = 84$

$x = 63$ The lesser number is $\dfrac{1}{3}x = \dfrac{1}{3}(63) = 21$.

GED SKILL BUILDER PRACTICE 5

1. **2/3** Let games lost $= x$ and games won $= 2x$. The difference between games won and lost is 5, so $2x - x = 5$, which means $x = 5$ and $2x = 10$. Add to find the total number of games played: $5 + 10 = 15$. The ratio of games won to games played is $\dfrac{10}{15} = \dfrac{2}{3}$.

2. **153.9** The radius is half the diameter. If $d = 14$, then $r = 7$. Use the formula for area of a circle: $A = \pi r^2 = \pi(7^2) = 153.86$, which rounds to 153.9.

3. **7/4 or 1.75** Let white $= x$, blue $= 3x$, and green $= \dfrac{3}{2}x$.

$x + 3x + \dfrac{3}{2}x = 9\dfrac{5}{8}$

$\dfrac{11}{2}x = \dfrac{77}{8}$

$x = \dfrac{7}{4} = 1.75$

4. **1/4 or .25 or 0.25** $-x + 5 = 3x + 4$

$1 = 4x$

$\dfrac{1}{4} = x$, and $\dfrac{1}{4} = 0.25$

5. **76** Add 6 meters to each measure and find the perimeter of the rectangular space. $P = 2l + 2w = 2(21) + 2(17) = 42 + 34 = 76$ meters

6. **8.75 or 35/4** Use the formula for area of a parallelogram. Note that 6 inches equals $\dfrac{1}{2}$ ft., or 0.5 ft.

$A = bh$

$A = 3.5 \times 2.5 = 8.75$ or

$A = 3\dfrac{1}{2} \times 2\dfrac{1}{2} = \dfrac{7}{2} \times \dfrac{5}{2} = \dfrac{35}{4}$

7. **12** Substitute -15 for y and solve for x.

$3x - 4(-15) = 96$

$3x + 60 = 96$

$3x = 36$

$x = 12$

8. **21/10** If the cyclist covers 24 miles, then it is 12 miles up and 12 miles down. Use the distance formula $d = rt$. On the way up: $12 = 8t$ and $t = \dfrac{12}{8} = \dfrac{3}{2} = 1\dfrac{1}{2}$ hr. $= 90$ min. On the way down: $12 = 20t$ and $t = \dfrac{12}{20} = \dfrac{3}{5}$ hr., or 36 min. Total time $= 126$ min or $\dfrac{3}{2} + \dfrac{3}{5} = \dfrac{15}{10} + \dfrac{6}{10} = \dfrac{21}{10}$.

9. **23.2** Add the sides to find the perimeter.

$5.1 + 8.7 + 9.4 = 23.2$

10. **1.8** Let the width $= w$ and the length $= 2w - 0.4$. Use the formula for perimeter of a rectangle. $P = 2l + 2w$

$10 = 2(2w - 0.4) + 2w$

$10 = 4w - 0.8 + 2w$

$10.8 = 6w$

$1.8 = w$

11. **4.875** Divide the ounces by the number of ounces in a pound. $78 \div 16 = 4.875$

12. **54** Think of adding the average height and an unknown height and dividing by two (the number of heights being added). Since the answer is to be in inches, convert to inches before solving: 4 ft. 1 in. = 4(12) + 1 = 49 in. and 4 ft. 2 in. = 4(12) + 2 = 50 in.

49 x 4 = 196

50 x 5 = 250

250 - 194 = 54 in.

THE COORDINATE PLANE, PAGES 76–79
GUIDED PRACTICE

1. **(-1, -3)** Since the two points have the same y-coordinate, so will the midpoint. The distance between -5 and 3 would be 8 spaces, so 4 spaces from either point would be the midpoint.

2. $\frac{1}{3}$ Use the slope formula $\frac{y_2 - y_1}{x_2 - x_1}$ to find the difference in the y-coordinates divided by the difference in the x-coordinates.

$$\frac{-3 - (-1)}{-3 - 3} = \frac{-3 + 1}{-6} = \frac{-2}{-6} = \frac{1}{3}$$

GED SKILL BUILDER PRACTICE 6

1. **(-2, 4)**   <insert art AK6, not provided>
2. **(4)** $\sqrt{68}$ Use the formula for finding the distance between points.

$$\sqrt{(x_2 - x_1)^2 + (y_2 - y_1)^2}$$
$$\sqrt{(-4 - 4)^2 + (-2 - 0)^2}$$
$$\sqrt{(-8)^2 + (-2)^2}$$
$$\sqrt{64 + 4} = \sqrt{68}$$

3. **(2, 0)** Since the two points have the same x-coordinate, so will the midpoint. The halfway distance between -4 and 4 is 0, so that would be the y-coordinate.

4. **(4) For every 5 feet forward, the hiker goes down 1 foot.** Draw a sketch. The slope shows rise/run. With a negative slope, the slope goes "downhill." With a run of 5, that's like a distance of 5. The rise is going down 1 foot for every 5 feet.

5. **(0, 0)** The only point on both axes is where the axes intersect, which is the origin at (0, 0).

6. **(-1, -3)** A point that is above or below another point has the same x-coordinate and a different y-coordinate. Count down or subtract 5 from 2, which equals -3. Point A is at (-1, -3).

7. **2** Find the difference in the y-coordinates divided by the difference in the x-coordinates.

$$\frac{-1 - 3}{2 - 4} = \frac{-4}{-2} = 2$$

8. **10** Use the formula for finding the distance between points.

$$\sqrt{(x_2 - x_1)^2 + (y_2 - y_1)^2}$$
$$\sqrt{(-4 - 2)^2 + (5 - (-3))^2}$$
$$\sqrt{(-6)^2 + (8)^2}$$
$$\sqrt{36 + 64} = \sqrt{100} = 10$$

9. **(2, 4)** Since the two points have the same y-coordinate, the midpoint will have a y-coordinate of 4. The distance between the x-coordinates would be 6 units (5 units on the positive x-axis and 1 unit on the negative x-axis). Half of 6 is 3, so move 3 spaces from one point to the other point. The midpoint is (2, 4).

10. $\frac{7}{11}$ Remember, slope is $\frac{\text{rise}}{\text{run}}$.

11. **10** Use the formula for finding the distance between points.

$$\sqrt{(x_2 - x_1)^2 + (y_2 - y_1)^2}$$
$$\sqrt{(-4 - 2)^2 + (-4 - 4)^2}$$
$$\sqrt{(-6)^2 + (-8)^2}$$
$$\sqrt{100} = 10$$

FIGURES ON THE COORDINATE PLANE, PAGES 80–83
GUIDED PRACTICE

1. **(3, 5)** The point will have the same x-coordinate as point C and the same y-coordinate as point A.

2. **(1, -3)** Rotating the figure 180° would put point A 4 units below point B at (1, -3).

GED SKILL BUILDER PRACTICE 7

1. **(-2, 1)** The diameter is 6 units (the distance from one side of the circle to the other side). The radius is half of 6, or 3. The center is 3 units in from any point on the circle.

2. **(-3, -4)** After flipping the triangle, segment PR would be across from -2 on the y-axis. Point Q would be 2 units lower at (-3, -4). The x-coordinate of point Q does not change.

3. **(-2, -4)** Point V will be directly across from point U, so it will have a y-coordinate of -4. Count the number of units between points S and T (7), and then count 7 units left from point U. Point V is at (-2, -4).

4. **(-2, 3)** You can either count up and over from point D or add 3 to the x-coordinate and 5 to the y-coordinate. Note that you would add because movements of up and right are both positive.

5. **(-5, -2)** Count the number of units between points X and Z. After the rotation, point X will be directly to the left of point Z. Count 7 units to the left of point Z. Point X will be at (-5, -2).

6. **(2, 3)** The only possible places for right angles are at points A and D, so count straight up from point A for the x-coordinate and straight over from point C for the y-coordinate.

7. **(-4, 4)** Point F is 3 units from segment EG. Flipping the figure over the y-axis would have segment EG directly above -1 on the x-axis. Count 3 units to the left of -1, and keep the y-coordinate at 4.

8. **(-4, -1)** Count 2 units to the left for the x-coordinate (-4) and 6 units down for the y-coordinate (-1).